ULTIMATE POCKET PUZZLES

# Wordsearch

## For Kids

ARCTURUS

**ARCTURUS**

This edition published in 2019 by Arcturus Publishing Limited
26/27 Bickels Yard, 151–153 Bermondsey Street,
London SE1 3HA

Copyright © Arcturus Holdings Limited

ISBN: 978-1-78888-482-2
CH006442NT
Supplier 40, Date 0119, Print run 7799

Illustrated by Memo Angeles (Shutterstock)
Edited by Becca Clunes

Printed in the UK

# CONTENTS

# HOW TO SOLVE A PUZZLE

Welcome to this book packed full of over 160 fun wordsearch puzzles!

Each puzzle consists of a grid of letters and a list of words, all of which are hidden somewhere in the grid. Your task is to ring each word as you find it, then mark it off the list, continuing until every word has been found.

Any letter in the grid might be used more than once in different words. For example, SEARCH and WORD might share the same letter:

Instructions on where the words might be found in each puzzle are given, but if you get stuck, don't worry, as answers to all of them can be found at the back of the book. Try not to peek!

# Beginners

## 1: FARM ANIMALS

Find all of these words in the grid.
Look across from left to right, and from
the top to the bottom of the grid.

```
P S H E E P A N Y P
H E C W P O N Y F I
E D U C K D C H W G
A S H V W A T C S L
U C H I C K E N D E
T H Z H R L A M B T
S O H C A L F H Z Q
T R A N I M A M Z F
E S G O O S E M Z U
N E B S Y X G O A T
```

| | |
|---|---|
| CALF | HORSE |
| CHICKEN | LAMB |
| DUCK | PIGLET |
| GOAT | PONY |
| GOOSE | SHEEP |

# Beginners

## 2: DIRECTIONS

Find all of these words in the grid.
Look across from left to right, and from
the top to the bottom of the grid.

```
C A O W S W E S T B
R U T F K L V Y U A
I D O W N W A R D C
G E S B Y N N C G K
H F E V S O U T H U
T W S U P W A R D E
P T F A R P E A I L
F S E L U F E A R E
H F O R W A R D Z F
E A S T N O R T H T
```

BACK ✓          NORTH

DOWNWARD ✓      RIGHT

EAST            SOUTH

FORWARD         UPWARD

LEFT            WEST

# Beginners

## 3: AT THE BEACH

Find all of these words in the grid.
Look across from left to right, and from
the top to the bottom of the grid.

```
S T A R F I S H E U
I E T S A N D E P S
V S W I M M I N G P
R S T I M E L A S H
S U R F E R U B B H
V U O E S E N D U E
I C E C R E A M C G
T O W E L R O C K S
E D S P A D E J E D
P E B B L E S F T I
```

BUCKET                SPADE

ICE CREAM             STARFISH

PEBBLES               SURFER

ROCKS                 SWIMMING

SAND                  TOWEL

# Beginners

## 4: PAINTBOX

Find all of these words in the grid.
Look across from left to right, and from
the top to the bottom of the grid.

```
W H I T E S V Z W G
O E T R E H C W P R
E V I O J E S D I E
P U R P L E N Y N E
K E A D Y C I J K N
B V I O L E T R E D
L W E O R A N G E V
A A C U Z O B L U E
C Y E L L O W E U I
K B I B E L U E S N
```

| | |
|---|---|
| BLACK | PURPLE |
| BLUE | RED |
| GREEN | VIOLET |
| ORANGE | WHITE |
| PINK | YELLOW |

# Beginners

## 5: UNDER THE GROUND

Find all of these words in the grid.
Look across from left to right, and from
the top to the bottom of the grid.

```
C T U N N E L M G L
E B A S E M E N T W
L L E S A R A S Y N
L L E A W D T U G B
A W E Y R O O T S T
R D R A I N H T X O
O E N D A B A J B W
P O T A T O I Q M O
G H E N A C A V E R
A M I N E M O L E M
```

| | |
|---|---|
| BASEMENT | MOLE |
| CAVE | POTATO |
| CELLAR | ROOTS |
| DRAIN | TUNNEL |
| MINE | WORM |

# Beginners

## 6: RAINY DAY

Find all of these words in the grid.
Look across from left to right, and from
the top to the bottom of the grid.

```
S A T A I W A T E R
P U D D L E N O R Y
L D R O P L E T S L
A G S E U G S C L U
S R A I N C O A T E
H S H O W E R A E A
U M B R E L L A L E
S E U D R I Z Z L E
E C J T Y S T O R M
C L O U D S S E O L
```

| | |
|---|---|
| CLOUDS | SHOWER |
| DRIZZLE | SPLASH |
| DROPLETS | STORM |
| PUDDLE | UMBRELLA |
| RAINCOAT | WATER |

# Beginners

## 7: MAKE LOTS OF NOISE

Find all of these words in the grid.
Look across from left to right, and from
the top to the bottom of the grid.

```
S C R E E C H E Z O
G E L E U R O A R S
C R E A K W A I L C
V E I F W W F S D R
Y E Y G T H S V K E
H R O R A I F M G A
I S L A M S V U U M
H O W L E T M E R O
R I N G G L R K S N
D E K E B E B O O M
```

BOOM            SCREAM

CREAK           SCREECH

HOWL            SLAM

RING            WAIL

ROAR            WHISTLE

# Beginners

## 8: BIRTHDAY PARTY

Find all of these words in the grid.
Look across from left to right, and from
the top to the bottom of the grid.

```
S E A M E G I F T S
C A N D L E S R X T
E U R T O C A R D S
P B V C A K E M Y M
B A L L O O N S I S
R E Y E H E F E E F
T H A P P Y O V V D
G A M E S B O B P E
H F R I E N D S U T
I N V I T A T I O N
```

| | |
|---|---|
| BALLOONS | FRIENDS |
| CAKE | GAMES |
| CANDLES | GIFTS |
| CARDS | HAPPY |
| FOOD | INVITATION |

# Beginners

## 9: EAT YOUR VEGETABLES

Find all of these words in the grid.
Look across from left to right, and from
the top to the bottom of the grid.

```
C A R R O T C A P P
A S P D U O N I O N
B S E T A P O N T Z
B E P R O A S G A V
A D P E A R E G T F
G I E N M S E S O E
E A R O E N S S E N
P U G S P I N A C H
T U R N I P C Z E D
L E T T U C E T E M
```

| | |
|---|---|
| CABBAGE | PEA |
| CARROT | PEPPER |
| LETTUCE | POTATO |
| ONION | SPINACH |
| PARSNIP | TURNIP |

# Beginners

## 10: CYCLING

Find all of these words in the grid.
Look across from left to right, and from
the top to the bottom of the grid.

```
N V F B I C Y C L E
R E P E D A L S G E
H E L M E T A Y O S
P O E P A S E P R P
V O Z Y B E L L I E
S A D D L E I U E M
L I G H T S P J V P
L E W R B R A K E S
Y U D W H E E L S H
G E A R S C H A I N
```

| | |
|---|---|
| BELL | HELMET |
| BICYCLE | LIGHTS |
| BRAKES | PEDALS |
| CHAIN | SADDLE |
| GEARS | WHEELS |

# Beginners

## 11: AT THE CIRCUS

Find all of these words in the grid.
Look across from left to right, and from
the top to the bottom of the grid.

```
H I G H W I R E T B
C L O W N S M R I I
T R I C K S C C G G
P A R A D E C A H T
P R H E P L T E T O
B A L L O O N S R P
T G E P K O I S O E
E N I M A G I C P H
R I N G M A S T E R
T R A P E Z E R D E
```

| BALLOONS | PARADE |
| BIG TOP | RINGMASTER |
| CLOWNS | TIGHTROPE |
| HIGH WIRE | TRAPEZE |
| MAGIC | TRICKS |

## 12: FIREWORK PARTY

Find all of these words in the grid.
Look across from left to right, and from
the top to the bottom of the grid.

```
F I Z Z I N G S Z G
S P A R K L E R V V
T U E L E V E V B F
F T B W H O O S H L
I E V X F L A R E I
D I S P L A Y O Y G
K A E A E U F C J H
F I R E W O R K S T
B A N G E R E E S S
N O I S Y Y U T E D
```

| | |
|---|---|
| BANGER | LIGHTS |
| DISPLAY | NOISY |
| FIREWORKS | ROCKET |
| FIZZING | SPARKLER |
| FLARE | WHOOSH |

# Beginners

## 13: BABY ANIMALS

Find all of these words in the grid.
Look across from left to right, and from
the top to the bottom of the grid.

```
F A W N P I G L E T
N E T I R A S E P V
D U C K L I N G U L
K I T T E N E V P F
K U B E Y U B R P C
H C O W G U S A Y H
F T A D P O L E W I
O G O E U I Z T C C
A E C U B L K R A K
L J E M R L A M B P
```

CHICK                KITTEN

CUB                  LAMB

DUCKLING             PIGLET

FAWN                 PUPPY

FOAL                 TADPOLE

# Beginners

## 14: CHRISTMAS

Find all of these words in the grid.
Look across from left to right, and from
the top to the bottom of the grid.

```
E C A N D Y M A S E
S H Z G I F T S A R
A H O L L Y W E S O
N F L L Q C A R D S
T R E E O L S E J T
A W U L I G H T S E
V W G T E A S P A N
U S O C B T T O Y S
L G L F P R A P J H
E C D E F M R V A E
```

| | |
|---|---|
| CANDY | LIGHTS |
| CARDS | SANTA |
| GIFTS | STAR |
| GOLD | TOYS |
| HOLLY | TREE |

# Beginners

## 15: OUT IN SPACE

Find all of these words in the grid.
Look across from left to right, and from
the top to the bottom of the grid.

```
P L A N E T S L X I
H T L B S M O O N B
J U P I T E R M M Q
P L U T O N Z Y O J
P A H L X C M A R S
U N E P T U N E R S
E U Y I Y T R A E T
I Y E M S U N I A A
S A T U R N D Z R R
U N E L V E N U S S
```

JUPITER          PLUTO

MARS             SATURN

MOON             STARS

NEPTUNE          SUN

PLANETS          VENUS

# Beginners

## 16: THINGS WITH WINGS

Find all of these words in the grid.
Look across from left to right, and from
the top to the bottom of the grid.

```
O S T R I C H E J H
S T R B E C C A F M
C G O O S E I G A O
W C O T A M V L I T
I O T M Y S M E R H
M E R A C R O W Y L
D R A G O N F L Y J
N P K A R A H O D O
B U T T E R F L Y F
A N G E L U B I R D
```

| | |
|---|---|
| ANGEL | EAGLE |
| BIRD | FAIRY |
| BUTTERFLY | GOOSE |
| CROW | MOTH |
| DRAGONFLY | OSTRICH |

## 17: WINNIE THE POOH

Find all of these words in the grid.
Look across from left to right, and from
the top to the bottom of the grid.

```
H E F F A L U M P G
U J W I N N E L I E
N P E P V E X R O O
N F T I G G E R I R
Y G L G R A B B I T
R O E L E E Y O R E
Y U E E C A W A S
F X A T I N K L H U
K A N G A S K A N N
W I N N I E S P H C
```

| | |
|---|---|
| EEYORE | PIGLET |
| HEFFALUMP | RABBIT |
| HUNNY | ROO |
| KANGA | TIGGER |
| OWL | WINNIE |

## 18: GARDEN CREATURES

Find all of these words in the grid.
Look across from left to right, and from
the top to the bottom of the grid.

```
M B U T T E R F L Y
I C E N T I P E D E
L M I J G A E S N J
L A N T R C W S F S
I W O R M E I L O P
P E O R M F Q U E I
E F E A R W I G N D
D I B E E T L E T E
E F E R H E F G W R
H A U I V S N A I L
```

| | |
|---|---|
| ANT | MILLIPEDE |
| BEETLE | SLUG |
| BUTTERFLY | SNAIL |
| CENTIPEDE | SPIDER |
| EARWIG | WORM |

# Beginners

## 19: IN THE AIR

Find all of these words in the grid.
Look across from left to right, and from
the top to the bottom of the grid.

```
G C L O U D W A E T
L A N B A L L O O N
I S T E A M M V B L
D E A R E S E C U I
E A A R E M A C B F
R K B I H R R Q B E
W I I P L A N E L P
A T R C A S T P E O
Y E D M O T H U E Y
P A R A C H U T E A
```

| | |
|---|---|
| BALLOON | KITE |
| BIRD | MOTH |
| BUBBLE | PARACHUTE |
| CLOUD | PLANE |
| GLIDER | STEAM |

# Beginners

## 20: HOMES FOR ANIMALS

Find all of these words in the grid.
Look across from left to right, and from
the top to the bottom of the grid.

```
E V G W E R A Y Q C
P E N H E A R E G H
R T Z C A H I V E U
P O N D M V M S E T
R Q O C W E B K G C
S T A B L E C L U H
E N S F I C A G A G
B E A C D N E S T F
D E N K E N N E L H
L A I R E F O H R N
```

| | |
|---|---|
| DEN | NEST |
| HIVE | PEN |
| HUTCH | POND |
| KENNEL | STABLE |
| LAIR | WEB |

# Beginners

## 21: JEWELS AND GEMS

Find all of these words in the grid.
Look across from left to right, and from
the top to the bottom of the grid.

```
T U R Q U O I S E C
U I S A P P H I R E
T O P A Z L U T G S
E G A R N E T E M E
U O P A L A Z P E P
O S W F O P E A R L
A E V R U B Y Z A E
S E M E R A L D R I
E D I A M O N D L R
J A D E N Y P A Z E
```

DIAMOND          PEARL

EMERALD          RUBY

GARNET           SAPPHIRE

JADE             TOPAZ

OPAL             TURQUOISE

# Beginners

## 22: DESERT ISLAND

Find all of these words in the grid.
Look across from left to right, and from
the top to the bottom of the grid.

```
C A V E S U Y E P G
E W D D F V U Y J U
H G E A R A F T A B
O C E A N K Q Z W X
R O C K S B E A C H
S H I P W R E C K U
S H E L T E R A F E
S P H J C L I F F S
L A G O O N D B I S
P H R E S C U E U K
```

| | |
|---|---|
| BEACH | RAFT |
| CAVES | RESCUE |
| CLIFFS | ROCKS |
| LAGOON | SHELTER |
| OCEAN | SHIPWRECK |

# Beginners

## 23: BATH TIME

Find all of these words in the grid.
Look across from left to right, and from
the top to the bottom of the grid.

```
A  F  E  R  A  N  E  T  A  S
V  E  W  P  L  U  G  G  R  B
E  T  S  F  E  E  R  A  V  U
T  I  L  E  D  B  A  T  H  B
C  O  L  D  W  A  T  E  R  B
T  O  W  E  L  S  O  A  P  L
W  D  R  Y  A  U  G  L  M  E
C  L  E  A  N  I  N  G  O  S
H  S  P  O  N  G  E  T  U  B
H  O  T  W  A  T  E  R  L  Z
```

| | |
|---|---|
| BATH | PLUG |
| BUBBLES | SOAP |
| CLEANING | SPONGE |
| COLD WATER | TOWEL |
| HOT WATER | TUB |

# Beginners

## 24: BUILDINGS

Find all of these words in the grid.
Look across from left to right, and from
the top to the bottom of the grid.

```
C I N E M A T J M J
C R N W M U S E U M
H O T E L J M T T P
L E A N A C T H O T
P A L A C E I E W U
E A C O T T A G E G
S A P L I B R A R Y
H O S P I T A L U A
R S C H O O L F G C
C A B I N H O U S E
```

| | |
|---|---|
| CABIN | HOUSE |
| CINEMA | LIBRARY |
| COTTAGE | MUSEUM |
| HOSPITAL | PALACE |
| HOTEL | SCHOOL |

# Beginners

## 25: IN THE PARK

Find all of these words in the grid.
Look across from left to right, and from
the top to the bottom of the grid.

```
F P A T H S P O N D
T R E E S L O G Y W
F I D A R I S T O R
L Y E N D I T R Y H
O D U C K S L E C D
W V E M B L E R S D
E C B U S H E S Y L
R A G R A S S V S A
S F T I D E L A R K
H E B I R D S H P E
```

| | |
|---|---|
| BIRDS | GRASS |
| BUSHES | LAKE |
| CAFE | PATHS |
| DUCKS | POND |
| FLOWERS | TREES |

# Beginners

### 26: PETER PAN

Find all of these words in the grid.
Look across from left to right, and from
the top to the bottom of the grid.

```
T B I N K E R B E D
I W E N D Y S Y Y N
G E O R R J O H N E
E C D W P E T E R V
R L E C U R L Y N E
L O G I A R N C A R
I C A N I R I K N L
L K B O Y W B A A A
Y H E M E R S A R N
C R O C O D I L E D
```

CLOCK                NEVERLAND

CROCODILE            NIBS

CURLY                PETER

JOHN                 TIGER LILY

NANA                 WENDY

# Beginners

## 27: KITCHEN ITEMS

Find all of these words in the grid.
Look across from left to right, and from
the top to the bottom of the grid.

```
A C U P B O A R D S
D P A N S I R R E H
I L F F R E E Z E R
S P L A T E S Y A P
H T F O R F O R K S
E E L O S W A E S A
S S F U G R A T E R
B O W L S W H I S K
D E A G H A L A S I
S H E L V E S E N D
```

BOWLS              GRATER

CUPBOARDS          PANS

DISHES             PLATES

FORKS              SHELVES

FREEZER            WHISK

# Beginners

## 28: VERY LARGE

Find all of these words in the grid.
Look across from left to right, and from
the top to the bottom of the grid.

```
V A S T G R E A T H
M F S J I I P V S U
A A O Y A F E A Y G
M N A B N R N P V E
M U E C T R I L J J
O E S T G J U M B O
T I M M E N S E L S
H M A S S I V E M K
H I C W B I G E L A
G E N O R M O U S W
```

| | |
|---|---|
| BIG | IMMENSE |
| ENORMOUS | JUMBO |
| GIANT | MAMMOTH |
| GREAT | MASSIVE |
| HUGE | VAST |

# Beginners

## 29: ON VACATION

Find all of these words in the grid.
Look across from left to right, and from
the top to the bottom of the grid.

```
E  N  E  G  N  I  L  T  X  Y
S  T  R  I  O  B  Z  R  P  C
A  I  R  P  O  R  T  A  A  A
O  B  U  R  E  C  S  I  Q  M
T  E  N  C  P  L  A  N  E  E
A  S  W  I  M  S  U  I  T  R
X  T  O  R  T  O  I  S  H  A
I  H  O  T  E  L  M  A  P  S
S  U  I  T  C  A  S  E  K  U
U  N  I  S  C  E  N  E  R  Y
```

| | |
|---|---|
| AIRPORT | SCENERY |
| CAMERA | SUITCASE |
| HOTEL | SWIMSUIT |
| MAPS | TAXI |
| PLANE | TRAIN |

## 30: YELLOW THINGS

Find all of these words in the grid.
Look across from left to right, and from
the top to the bottom of the grid.

```
D U C K L I N G C O
C H I C K S C E N A
D A N D E L I O N E
L E N E G G Y O L K
D B U T T E R C U P
C A N A R Y X I L A
O N C C H E E S E I
D A F F O D I L M B
I N T R A S E W O E
V A B E N E N S N E
```

BANANA          DAFFODIL

BUTTERCUP       DANDELION

CANARY          DUCKLING

CHEESE          EGG YOLK

CHICKS          LEMON

# Beginners

## 31: WINTER

Find all of these words in the grid.
Look across from left to right, and from
the top to the bottom of the grid.

```
C T C A L A R Y C X
H S N O W M A N H V
R E I N A R I Y I I
I I C I C L E D L D
S K A T I N G N L L
T T I F R O S T Y S
M F R E E Z I N G C
A G R I N D L E X A
S U S S K I I N G R
S N O W B A L L T F
```

CHILLY            SCARF

CHRISTMAS      SKATING

FREEZING         SKIING

FROSTY            SNOWBALL

ICICLE             SNOWMAN

# Beginners

## 32: TEDDY BEAR

Find all of these words in the grid.
Look across from left to right, and from
the top to the bottom of the grid.

```
F R I E N D L Y S T
C L O C T E D D Y H
I J E R A N E A R N
E C U D D L Y F U R
A I A H P A W S E G
R X U L D S U F H E
S R I B B O N F B C
T W E B R E N B Y U
R O V F L U F F Y T
S Q U E A K E R T E
```

CUDDLY          FUR

CUTE            PAWS

EARS            RIBBON

FLUFFY          SQUEAKER

FRIENDLY        TEDDY

# Beginners

## 33: SNOW WHITE

Find all of these words in the grid.
Look across from left to right, and from
the top to the bottom of the grid.

```
G R U M P Y S A N P
B L O O A H A P P Y
S L E E P Y O A S E
E F A I R E S T T E
L E I B A S H F U L
D O C O E T R E R D
E N U M I R R O R A
D O P E Y A V E R A
M I S T Y A P P L E
W E B N S N E E Z Y
```

| | |
|---|---|
| APPLE | GRUMPY |
| BASHFUL | HAPPY |
| DOC | MIRROR |
| DOPEY | SLEEPY |
| FAIREST | SNEEZY |

## 34: PETS

Find all of these words in the grid.
Look across from left to right, and from
the top to the bottom of the grid.

```
C R A B B I T R E C
R S E M K I T T E N
O H O R S E W E R S
G C M H A M S T E R
U A H E M D O G E R
K T G N O D A D V E
P U P P Y U E N A R
V I S T U C F R O G
T I E L O K L P X S
I A G O L D F I S H
```

| | |
|---|---|
| CAT | HAMSTER |
| DOG | HORSE |
| DUCK | KITTEN |
| FROG | PUPPY |
| GOLDFISH | RABBIT |

# Beginners

## 35: FABRICS

Find all of these words in the grid.
Look across from left to right, and from
the top to the bottom of the grid.

```
U F T O S A T I N E
O L V E L V E T E M
N Y L O N G Q V L E
T R I S C O T T O N
G E S K S I L K N D
A M V B C Z B C D O
I L L I N E N F E Y
S A B A I S X E N N
E C C V W O O L I A
D E B E E J L T M M
```

| | |
|---|---|
| COTTON | NYLON |
| DENIM | SATIN |
| FELT | SILK |
| LACE | VELVET |
| LINEN | WOOL |

# Beginners

## 36: MUSICAL INSTRUMENTS

Find all of these words in the grid.
Look across from left to right, and from
the top to the bottom of the grid.

```
D A T R I A N G L E
R I H A R P D R U M
E H E E S I O B O E
C O R D E C D G F B
O R N O R G A N L A
R N B A N J O G U H
D R N P S E R A T F
E D C L A R I N E T
R A Q N L U U T V H
E R Y E E T R I A N
```

| | |
|---|---|
| BANJO | HORN |
| CLARINET | OBOE |
| DRUM | ORGAN |
| FLUTE | RECORDER |
| HARP | TRIANGLE |

# Beginners

## 37: LETS HAVE A PICNIC

Find all of these words in the grid.
Look across from left to right, and from
the top to the bottom of the grid.

```
B L E M O N A D E O
U E S A L A D C M T
T N S G F R U I T O
T E E S E C L O T H
E T M A L E S E C A
R P L E A B R E A D
W O N E Y E U S K W
F A R F P L A T E S
S C H E E S E Y S C
S A N D W I C H E S
```

BREAD            FRUIT

BUTTER           LEMONADE

CAKES            PLATES

CHEESE           SALAD

CLOTH            SANDWICHES

# Beginners

## 38: SO SOFT

Find all of these words in the grid.
Look across from left to right, and from
the top to the bottom of the grid.

```
G E N T L E D O R A
V E L V E T Y E A L
S H O I D S I L K Y
F S Q U I S H Y E L
L E B G F L E E C Y
U G S U L L D I F D
F G E R I S A N U O
F E A T H E R Y R W
Y E D M P E T O R N
S M O O T H R O Y Y
```

| | |
|---|---|
| DOWNY | GENTLE |
| FEATHERY | SILKY |
| FLEECY | SMOOTH |
| FLUFFY | SQUISHY |
| FURRY | VELVETY |

# Beginners

## 39: LITTLE THINGS

Find all of these words in the grid.
Look across from left to right, and from
the top to the bottom of the grid.

```
R A I N D R O P T G
O E B K C H I C K N
U N S T A V F L E A
C P L E F A I R Y Y
R T M W B I M Y A W
U M A N T D O T M R
M E Y B E D A R I E
B L V A D M E K E E
I F M K H S E E D A
S N O W F L A K E R
```

| | |
|---|---|
| ANT | FAIRY |
| CHICK | FLEA |
| CRUMB | RAINDROP |
| DOT | SEED |
| ELF | SNOWFLAKE |

# Beginners

**40**: SOUP

Find all of these words in the grid.
Look across from left to right, and from
the top to the bottom of the grid.

```
C A R A O N I O N T
E K S T E R I N P O
L O X T A I L G E M
E P O T A T O E N A
R M U S H R O O M T
Y H U I I D A N E O
V E G E T A B L E A
P U M P K I N P O P
P E R S A T U P E A
L E Y C H I C K E N
```

CELERY          PEA

CHICKEN         POTATO

MUSHROOM        PUMPKIN

ONION           TOMATO

OXTAIL          VEGETABLE

# Beginners

**41:** MAGICAL

Find all of these words in the grid.
Look across from left to right, and from
the top to the bottom of the grid.

```
W I Z A R D S J W S
I Z A T Z S P N W E
T F A I R E E R A E
C A E L V C L E N V
H R L R F R L A D I
A P I X I E S V E C
E L V E S T E O A Z
E S M A G I C I A N
N O N F A I R I E S
T R I C K S N E C E
```

ELVES            SPELLS

FAIRIES          TRICKS

MAGICIAN         WAND

PIXIES           WITCH

SECRET           WIZARD

# Beginners

## 42: PIRATES

Find all of these words in the grid.
Look across from left to right, and from
the top to the bottom of the grid.

```
O G O L D S H I P S
P I R A E G T C A S
E Y E P A T C H R I
O F E R N A T T R L
E J E W E L S E O V
R R F B O W S E T E
C A P T A I N U D R
T J C H E S D R N Y
E M G N E A R M A P
O C E A N C H E S T
```

| CAPTAIN | MAP |
|---------|-----|
| CHEST | OCEAN |
| EYEPATCH | PARROT |
| GOLD | SHIP |
| JEWELS | SILVER |

# Beginners

**43: WASHING A CAR**

Find all of these words in the grid.
Look across from left to right, and from
the top to the bottom of the grid.

```
I Y E K W A T E R S
N I O T A F D Y O P
N B U C K E T H R O
H R A T E I N G Y N
P O L I S H E N E G
Z C L E A N I N G E
S K F W H E E L S S
O E A W I N D O W S
A S H I N E J B Y C
P S R I N S I N G E
```

BUCKET          SOAP

CLEANING        SPONGE

POLISH          WATER

RINSING         WHEELS

SHINE           WINDOWS

# Beginners

## 44: THINGS THAT CAN BE LOST

Find all of these words in the grid.
Look across from left to right, and from
the top to the bottom of the grid.

```
K E Y S K E P C B N
T R E A S U R E U M
S A S L E E P U T E
H O M E W O R K T M
E T T A S E S A O O
H E E L M G B I N R
S M E A A A B E E Y
E P T B H M O N E Y
O E H A P E U S E G
P R O V E R A N C E
```

| | |
|---|---|
| BUTTON | MONEY |
| GAME | SLEEP |
| HOMEWORK | TEETH |
| KEYS | TEMPER |
| MEMORY | TREASURE |

# Beginners

## 45: TRANSPORT

Find all of these words in the grid.
Look across from left to right, and from
the top to the bottom of the grid.

```
E X E M Y S H I P R
C Y A C H T T B K O
A H Y E W N R I H C
N F N S B W A C E K
O C U D V K I Y V E
E C T A X I N C C T
U R W B O A T L H P
J H O R S E L E L E
E I E L I Y A E H T
Q E Z T L P L A N E
```

BICYCLE          ROCKET

BOAT             SHIP

CANOE            TAXI

HORSE            TRAIN

PLANE            YACHT

## 46: SCHOOL

Find all of these words in the grid.
Look across from left to right, and from
the top to the bottom of the grid.

```
B O H I S T O R Y Y
O Y E C A S T N S Y
O E L A D E S K Y T
K L A A B C A R E B
S G E O G R A P H Y
C L A S S D E A K S
L E A R N I N G E P
T E A C H E R E I O
M U S I C U E R V R
G R E A D I N G Q T
```

| | |
|---|---|
| BOOKS | LEARNING |
| CLASS | MUSIC |
| DESK | READING |
| GEOGRAPHY | SPORT |
| HISTORY | TEACHER |

# Beginners

### 47: CALENDAR

Find all of these words in the grid.
Look across from left to right, and from
the top to the bottom of the grid.

```
E R T D A T E S N W
T U E S A J S E E E
S A T U R D A Y H E
T U E S D A Y T U K
W E D N E S D A Y S
I E L F R I D A Y E
T H U R S D A Y W K
M O N D M O N T H S
M O N D A Y E E N A
S U N D A Y K A E S
```

| | |
|---|---|
| DATES | SUNDAY |
| FRIDAY | THURSDAY |
| MONDAY | TUESDAY |
| MONTHS | WEDNESDAY |
| SATURDAY | WEEKS |

## 48: FEED THE ANIMALS

Find all of these words in the grid.
Look across from left to right, and from
the top to the bottom of the grid.

```
A P P L E S L O E T
C O R N M A R A O S
P T L T A Y A T D E
J V T G I E R S U A
G H U Y Z E K X F T
R R E M E T N U T S
A L E A V E S G E S
S B M E A S D A S A
S D W H E A T E A N
S E E D S U E H A Y
```

| | |
|---|---|
| APPLES | MAIZE |
| CORN | NUTS |
| GRASS | OATS |
| HAY | SEEDS |
| LEAVES | WHEAT |

# Beginners

**49: PIZZA**

Find all of these words in the grid.
Look across from left to right, and from
the top to the bottom of the grid.

```
P I N E A P P L E E
T F C P D R E A S Y
O H M E H I A H A M
M E C P T F J O E H
A E H P U E A T U D
T S E E N C R U S T
O A E R A A R E R E
E I S S O N I O N S
S C E O L I V E S B
M U S H R O O M S S
```

| | |
|---|---|
| CHEESE | ONIONS |
| CRUST | PEPPERS |
| HAM | PINEAPPLE |
| MUSHROOMS | TOMATOES |
| OLIVES | TUNA |

# Beginners

## 50: CINDERELLA

Find all of these words in the grid.
Look across from left to right, and from
the top to the bottom of the grid.

```
C A R I A G K V G C
R S P R I N C E P A
M I D N I G H T A R
D R E S S E U L L R
G N A S E T A F A I
Q U E E N P I R C A
B A L L P A L C E G
R A G S M I C E S E
S L I P P E R K N K
S Y R L I P E T E R
```

BALL            PALACE

CARRIAGE        PRINCE

DRESS           QUEEN

MICE            RAGS

MIDNIGHT        SLIPPER

# Beginners

## 51: REPTILES

Find all of these words in the grid.
Look across from left to right, and from
the top to the bottom of the grid.

```
A L L I G A T O R H
T T E R R A P I N E
O T E R R L Y L C W
R C A V I P E R G W
T U R T L E D P E D
O U E D J B S O C E
I G U A N A N Q K T
S R A J P Y T H O N
E C R O C O D I L E
L I Z A R D C L A R
```

| | |
|---|---|
| ALLIGATOR | PYTHON |
| CROCODILE | TERRAPIN |
| GECKO | TORTOISE |
| IGUANA | TURTLE |
| LIZARD | VIPER |

## 52: FLOWERS

Find all of these words in the grid.
Look across from left to right, and from
the top to the bottom of the grid.

```
C L A V E N D E R E
R S R I L I P U R A
O R C H I D L A P O
C D A F F O D I L P
U Y A M C O V E R P
S N O W D R O P N V
H D A I S Y I R I S
S U N F L O W E R L
L D E R A L I L Y O
N R P O P P Y A P Y
```

CROCUS              LILY

DAFFODIL            ORCHID

DAISY               POPPY

IRIS                SNOWDROP

LAVENDER            SUNFLOWER

# Beginners

## 53: BALL GAMES

Find all of these words in the grid.
Look across from left to right, and from
the top to the bottom of the grid.

```
E B A S E B A L L T
G E R E S H O S A E
D E B B T E N N I S
F M B O W L I N G T
S K I T T L E S O R
H O C K E Y C L L E
F O O T B A L L F G
B A S K E T B A L L
V P O L O O E R A L
R I N P O O L N C E
```

| | |
|---|---|
| BASEBALL | HOCKEY |
| BASKETBALL | POLO |
| BOWLING | POOL |
| FOOTBALL | SKITTLES |
| GOLF | TENNIS |

# Beginners

## 54: APPLE

Find all of these words in the grid.
Look across from left to right, and from
the top to the bottom of the grid.

```
F I A P P L D E N H
M O R C H A R D C W
C O R E N S E E D U
T R E E R G R E E N
P E E L J U I C Y S
S T R E R L S C I T
A I Y M E E A S E E
P B L O S S O M S M
E I I B K F R C K E
D Z O B R E D P Y S
```

| | |
|---|---|
| BLOSSOM | PEEL |
| CORE | RED |
| GREEN | SEED |
| JUICY | STEM |
| ORCHARD | TREE |

# Beginners

## 55: WHAT TO WEAR

Find all of these words in the grid.
Look across from left to right, and from
the top to the bottom of the grid.

```
C O A T G S A R B H
G S A C K C A J S S
L K G M L A D S O H
O L E A M R U H C O
V M E S G F V I K R
E J E A N S C R S T
S V A F U J U T C S
S W E A T E R O E O
S W I M S U I T A E
R K R P S K I R T I
```

| | |
|---|---|
| COAT | SHORTS |
| GLOVES | SKIRT |
| JEANS | SOCKS |
| SCARF | SWEATER |
| SHIRT | SWIMSUIT |

# Beginners

## 56: TIME FOR BED

Find all of these words in the grid.
Look across from left to right, and from
the top to the bottom of the grid.

```
C O C O A B L E E B
K B E A R A U Z S L
N S T O R Y L G H A
N E G F E U L M E N
T I R E D E A R E K
P I L L O W B H T E
S T A R Y S Y M S T
E E Y A W N I N G E
E M M A T T R E S S
G O O D N I G H T R
```

| | |
|---|---|
| BLANKET | PILLOW |
| COCOA | SHEETS |
| GOODNIGHT | STORY |
| LULLABY | TIRED |
| MATTRESS | YAWNING |

# Gentle

## 57: CONTAINERS

Find all of these words in the grid.
Look up, down, and across.
Words can run backward as well as forward.

```
B O O T F B A R R E L Q
D E E E S U I T C A S E
Y K O K R S T J U A S T
E C P S B T E A N Q S U
S X B A W U B E K E A D
W O A C U E P L F R L J
Z B C A R E K C O L G B
E L K E L T T O B F V B
T O P H A B E G O E S O
A O A F C E A U W R Y R
R T C J F H E J L L E F
C Y K P O C K E T E I V
```

| BACKPACK | CASKET | LOCKER |
| BARREL | CRATE | POCKET |
| BOTTLE | GLASS | SUITCASE |
| BOWL | JUG | TOOLBOX |

# Gentle

## 58: MADE OF PAPER

Find all of these words in the grid.
Look up, down, and across.
Words can run backward as well as forward.

```
G I F T T A G D I A R Y
E R A I H E U N E M G C
E T A H H U S P O R M E
V S M F H S Y E X O S N
L R A C I S E F O U I V
U E P O T I B A R L B E
S T R M T T I U Q U U L
J S B I E U S O B E S O
E O E C F S U P D T K P
T P U C N K E L C I O E
P S L Q O S G A B K O J
N Y Q X C E N A S F B V
```

BAGS              DIARY             MAP

BOOK              ENVELOPE          MENU

COMIC             GIFT TAG          POSTER

CONFETTI          KITE              TISSUE

# Gentle

## 59: NUTS AND SEEDS

Find all of these words in the grid.
Look up, down, and across.
Words can run backward as well as forward.

```
N U T K U B P E C A N A
E O I H C A T S I P J F
B C C N I K P M U P D C
R A R L R C A S H E W A
A S T F E N N E L C U R
Z E H C S C D N O M L A
I P E A N U T W G Z T W
L E A I Y J T M B G U A
Y H S U S E S A M E N Y
A L L I D N B C R A L X
Q I G B M T B A R E A H
I B U O C B S E A V W A
```

| ALMOND | DILL | PISTACHIO |
|--------|------|-----------|
| BRAZIL | FENNEL | PUMPKIN |
| CARAWAY | PEANUT | SESAME |
| CASHEW | PECAN | WALNUT |

# Gentle

## 60: PAIRS OF THINGS

Find all of these words in the grid.
Look up, down, and across.
Words can run backward as well as forward.

| | | | | | | | | | | | |
|---|---|---|---|---|---|---|---|---|---|---|---|
| L | U | N | G | S | G | L | O | V | E | S | V |
| I | A | B | U | G | L | L | I | L | E | P | E |
| N | S | C | I | S | S | O | R | S | T | P | Y |
| E | E | N | T | E | J | W | C | S | E | H | E |
| A | R | W | C | Y | C | D | W | L | N | G | S |
| P | E | I | U | N | S | D | N | A | H | R | I |
| L | S | N | G | Y | K | L | E | S | F | A | M |
| E | K | G | T | G | B | J | D | N | M | Y | M |
| S | C | S | E | J | Y | S | K | A | T | E | S |
| A | O | K | D | D | R | L | T | E | H | C | R |
| J | S | E | O | H | S | Z | G | J | S | I | F |
| H | Q | J | I | T | E | E | F | H | E | D | R |

| | | |
|---|---|---|
| DICE | HANDS | SHOES |
| EYES | JEANS | SKATES |
| FEET | LUNGS | SOCKS |
| GLOVES | SCISSORS | WINGS |

# Gentle

## 61: SUMMER

Find all of these words in the grid.
Look up, down, and across.
Words can run backward as well as forward.

```
S Z H E T C N S E A S G
L K T Y E I A U N E Y F
O M M L D N R H I W N S
R A R T A C L L H H E B
J E A Y N I S S S W O L
B R W Y O P E A N F M T
E C P C M M S L U P E L
A E E Z E M O A S D A I
C C F E L S R D F I D H
H I S T R O H S O E O A
G N I F R U S F E T W D
A V S L O S A R A P S L
```

BEACH          PARASOL        SHORTS

ICE CREAM      PICNIC         SUNSHINE

LEMONADE       ROSES          SURFING

MEADOWS        SALAD          WARMTH

# Gentle

## 62: WILD CATS

Find all of these words in the grid.
Look up, down, and across.
Words can run backward as well as forward.

```
G N A N I M E N E Z P T
U A H I I H L I O N J O
C O U G A R T K E C F L
T E C T A C B O B H R E
Y A G R A M P D A E A C
S P M C R J E T W E U O
E K H K E L Y N X T G S
S C D G H M E R R A A D
E N S P T A W I E H J A
A C V Z N K K F G O T E
L E O P A R D M I D Y E
D A M U P I P I T O H D
```

BOBCAT            LEOPARD           OCELOT

CHEETAH           LION              PANTHER

COUGAR            LYNX              PUMA

JAGUAR            MARGAY            TIGER

# Gentle

## 63: SALAD

Find all of these words in the grid.
Look up, down, and across.
Words can run backward as well as forward.

```
D S S X A R S B R E H A
F N X R A E L E F N U E
U O Y U G B O D I U P M
I I R J D M T Y T K E I
I N E T E U A C Y S P J
H O L R V C M P I E P L
C R E S S U O Q U V E T
Q A C X R C T W M I R Y
L E T T U C E D V L O A
I O T O R R A C R O P E
O S P O T A T O H A Q I
T J E N A B E B P E A S
```

| CARROT | HERBS | PEAS |
|--------|-------|------|
| CELERY | LETTUCE | PEPPER |
| CRESS | OLIVES | POTATO |
| CUCUMBER | ONIONS | TOMATO |

# Gentle

**64**: SAFARI PARK

Find all of these words in the grid.
Look up, down, and across.
Words can run backward as well as forward.

```
F R N F E R I D A S C O
V E S K F M E E R K A T
T G L B A B O O N O I L
H I A G U V A W B D I C
Y T M S R O T I S I V F
E M I W O M E A M I L A
M N N C G G T F O Y F E
K E A E R A N G E R W T
Q D M I V O S T R I C H
G R A A O T Y E K N O M
V A L L A U C E E M Z U
K W L T H G U I D E S A
```

ANIMALS          LLAMA          RANGER

BABOON           MEERKAT        TIGER

GUIDES           MONKEY         VISITORS

LION             OSTRICH        WARDEN

# Gentle

### 65: JEWELS AND TRINKETS

Find all of these words in the grid.
Look up, down, and across.
Words can run backward as well as forward.

```
E C A L K C E N K G E K
T G L A C S I Z E N U P
E Y P E N L N M M I Q D
L B E F I R W A U R G U
E U M H E A O A D S E E
C S S Q O E R B N V F D
A E B H X P C B E A D S
R J T N A D N E P S C T
B E E Y P L K U T U H I
E D A I L O C K E T A A
P E L G N A B U H K I R
S U R W B R O O C H N A
```

BANGLE          CHAIN           PEARLS

BEADS           CROWN           PENDANT

BRACELET        LOCKET          RING

BROOCH          NECKLACE        TIARA

## Gentle

### 66: FACE

Find all of these words in the grid.
Look up, down, and across.
Words can run backward as well as forward.

```
G E S S M I L E S B P F
S S E S W O R B E Y E L
N W L R E S D M Z L I A
W R P L I A F N I H C M
O E M X C K O J O C E B
R I I T B F R O Y H L M
F K D U R P E B O E K O
T C J E F S H V O E C U
L T I A J E E R K E T
S R A E Z T A S P K R H
Y N L I P S D A F L F E
Y E Y E L A S H E S I Y
```

| CHEEK | EYEBROWS | FROWN |
|-------|----------|-------|
| CHIN | EYELASHES | LIPS |
| DIMPLES | FOREHEAD | MOUTH |
| EARS | FRECKLE | SMILE |

# Gentle

67: TOYS

Find all of these words in the grid.
Look up, down, and across.
Words can run backward as well as forward.

```
R E T O O C S B S L E D
Z L F E B S T Y O Y O E
T T R E T K I M T A M G
E T D A R C L E H R O S
P A L B O I T K I T E N
P R U E Y R S L V Y L S
U L E E K B L J Q Y V E
P R A E B Y D D E T S L
T H E N Y P S J W E M B
F O E L C Y C I R T K R
I E R Y O U A G U R A A
T R I C S S L I D E Z M
```

| | | |
|---|---|---|
| BRICKS | RATTLE | STILTS |
| KITE | SCOOTER | TEDDY BEAR |
| MARBLES | SLED | TRICYCLE |
| PUPPET | SLIDE | YO-YO |

# Gentle

## 68: CREATURES' FEATURES

Find all of these words in the grid.
Look up, down, and across.
Words can run backward as well as forward.

```
N R I N T H E A R A T S
S H E L L B S K S U T R
S N I F M T W G U B Q E
K J N C O A T C A V N K
A L L W Z S S C A L E S
E T A L O N S R S R U I
B E E E S H A U P Y A H
P J V O P C N F O C P W
E Y P N D W A S T B H J
S C S L L I U Q S V I S
V N L B E R B A T E C V
H U S E N I P S A F V H
```

| | | |
|------|--------|----------|
| BEAK | QUILLS | SPOTS |
| COAT | SCALES | TALONS |
| FINS | SHELL | TUSKS |
| FUR | SPINES | WHISKERS |

# Gentle

Find all of these words in the grid.
Look up, down, and across.
Words can run backward as well as forward.

```
S E F T N E C S E R C G
T S H A P E V U E D N V
R H N E S T A T C U B E
A Q L A V O B E G C E V
E L G N A I R T T V L R
H V D R L P S V U H C D
D I M A R Y P V C H R I
E I E D C L H J R S I A
M D J Y T L E L O M C R
E R S Q U A R E S A D O
E V B H P B E E S I C I
D N O M A I D S T A R W
```

| | | |
|---|---|---|
| CIRCLE | DIAMOND | SPHERE |
| CRESCENT | HEART | SQUARE |
| CROSS | OVAL | STAR |
| CUBE | PYRAMID | TRIANGLE |

# Gentle

## 70: IN THE POND

Find all of these words in the grid.
Look up, down, and across.
Words can run backward as well as forward.

```
C E R A S E N O T S F P
V N P H S D A O T K B D
F X M F R A G S E T R A
R A U H S G O R F P P J
R I P P L E T S I E B S
A C Q V N E W T S B A T
R E T A W S R L C B C N
E S S M C K K G C L E A
U L G N H C F L A E K L
R E F L E O W B R S K P
C T A E C R C B P F L D
N O I T C E L F E R F W
```

| | | |
|---|---|---|
| CARP | PLANTS | ROCKS |
| FROGS | PUMP | STONES |
| NEWTS | REFLECTION | TOADS |
| PEBBLES | RIPPLE | WATER |

# Gentle

## 71: STORMY WEATHER

Find all of these words in the grid.
Look up, down, and across.
Words can run backward as well as forward.

```
M O N T H U N A E W S M
N O O S N O M I S D E R
D I S M C O R A L P L O
E N A C I R R U H K A T
B L L T O R N A D O G S
M E D H U P T A E S N L
L P E H P M D K B R O I
Y D N I W G R N R E O A
C R E D N U H T E W H H
C L O U D S E M E O P S
T O R N B T V Q Z H Y G
U T Y P H Y L O Y S T M
```

| | | |
|---|---|---|
| BREEZY | HAILSTORM | THUNDER |
| CLOUDS | HURRICANE | TORNADO |
| GALES | MONSOON | TYPHOON |
| GUSTY | SHOWERS | WINDY |

# Gentle

## 72: THINGS WE LOVE

Find all of these words in the grid.
Look up, down, and across.
Words can run backward as well as forward.

```
G R A N A D P G E C R L
T G N I M M I W S I S N
H Y I C I C L E S S Y E
S E G N I D R F Z U O S
Y D N A C K G N N M T I
E J F I R E W O R K S N
U J F J R E P R E I F G
H A P D N A R G M T S I
J H M E H T N P E T E N
L A U G H I N G V E K G
A O S O Y A L B Y N A I
G R A N D M A A U S C Y
```

| | | |
|---|---|---|
| CAKES | GRANDPA | MUSIC |
| CANDY | ICICLES | SINGING |
| FIREWORKS | KITTENS | SWIMMING |
| GRANDMA | LAUGHING | TOYS |

# Gentle

## 73: TOOLS

Find all of these words in the grid.
Look up, down, and across.
Words can run backward as well as forward.

```
M A P P I P J R A M R R
S Y B F H C N E R W A K
S U N M Z U S K P B B L
J I G R E N N A P S W E
E A S R E C N I P C O S
S E V W M E R I A R R I
P S C P L I E R S A C H
L L I R D I S K N P S C
A R P E N C I F O E X W
N H A M M E R T O R U I
E S C R E W D R I V E R
C T T A P P W A S N L I
```

| CHISEL | PINCERS | SCRAPER |
| CROWBAR | PLANE | SCREWDRIVER |
| DRILL | PLIERS | SPANNER |
| HAMMER | SAW | WRENCH |

# Gentle

**74: RED THINGS**

Find all of these words in the grid.
Look up, down, and across.
Words can run backward as well as forward.

```
H T O O G E R A S A R G
E I S G R U B I E S F O
A P E G A R N E T Y K I
R L S P P E L W G R E A
T U O T E U R N J R S L
V M R Y L O B S T E R O
O S H S E L H E G B E R
R L A R O C B G X W E T
P D N E H U C K P A L D
S Y R A S P B E H R P H
Y P P O P D H D P T P E
J Z O Y R R E B P S A R
```

| APPLE | HEART | RASPBERRY |
|-------|-------|-----------|
| CORAL | LOBSTER | ROSES |
| GARNET | PLUMS | RUBIES |
| GRAPE | POPPY | STRAWBERRY |

# Gentle

## 75: DIFFERENT TASTES

Find all of these words in the grid.
Look up, down, and across.
Words can run backward as well as forward.

```
F A Y G N A T R A N E S
I R F Z F R U I T Y E J
R U I T Y A G S R C Q B
E N V O S N K U N E M D
T S W E E T T G Y E Y C
T E H P E U I A C R Y Y
I M R E S O U R I R M H
B M E P M A G Y P O A S
B I T P O P A R S Z E I
B T R E R M I N T Y R F
R I V R C H E E S Y C F
L B E Y P C R E M Y A S
```

| | | |
|---|---|---|
| BITTER | FRUITY | SPICY |
| CHEESY | MINTY | SUGARY |
| CREAMY | PEPPERY | SWEET |
| FISHY | SOUR | TANGY |

# Gentle

## 76: SPORTS AND GAMES

Find all of these words in the grid.
Look up, down, and across.
Words can run backward as well as forward.

```
V L H J Q G F O O T A I
L L C C A N O E I N G G
V A T L G I S E R A S C
O B O W N N J O R S M U
L T C V I N E C I I J H
L O S Q L U K D D N O O
E O P P W R O W I N G C
Y F O E O A D B N E G K
B E H L B P S K G T I E
A S P R I N T I N G N Y
L L N A Y E R A Y M G F
L N Y H I C K E Y A E S
```

| BOWLING | HOPSCOTCH | RUNNING |
| --- | --- | --- |
| CANOEING | JOGGING | SPRINTING |
| FOOTBALL | RIDING | TENNIS |
| HOCKEY | ROWING | VOLLEYBALL |

# Gentle

## 77: HAUNTED HOUSE

Find all of these words in the grid.
Look up, down, and across.
Words can run backward as well as forward.

```
S M A E R C S T S T R I
E S C O B W E H C Y S G
E B C D C G I U I B W N
Y E E K L E T N E C O I
R W R P A H X D S R D L
E B N N N E G E T E A I
T O E O K O H R H A H A
S C O I I C O S G K S W
Y H U S N A S T I I R R
M C R E G R T O R N Z L
B T H S N O A R F G A E
Y R A C S T M M P C V S
```

CLANKING          GHOST          SCREAMS

COBWEBS           MYSTERY        SHADOWS

CREAKING          NOISES         THUNDERSTORM

FRIGHT            SCARY          WAILING

# Gentle

## 78: HOLES AND SPACES

Find all of these words in the grid.
Look up, down, and across.
Words can run backward as well as forward.

```
B C R A T E R N I A R D
B U R R U B I N A S T W
H E C R N S L E A T A O
H O T Y N S R L P G C R
G A T T E E F Y U W Y R
N N U J L C T C N O O U
I E C I V E R C C L M B
N F W A R R E N T L U H
E I P L C S N Q U O E T
P E R U S B C B R H U U
O G S L I V H O E V D N
I P I N H O L E C A W S
```

| | | |
|---|---|---|
| BURROW | HOLLOW | RECESS |
| CRATER | OPENING | TRENCH |
| CREVICE | PINHOLE | TUNNEL |
| DRAIN | PUNCTURE | WARREN |

# Gentle

## 79: A WALK IN THE WOODS

Find all of these words in the grid.
Look up, down, and across.
Words can run backward as well as forward.

```
S T O S E E B W O R C E
F R I O Z L O S C E T V
N U S E W T O A D A H L
G N I R A E L C A O W E
V K C E A E S E M I C R
U O W L S B L N U U K R
I R E K C E P D O O W I
S N H Y N G K Y C R U U
N B I R C H E T G E I Q
R E S T R I A N R E V S
T O A D S T O O L D Y W
G R A M O O R H S U M D
```

| | | |
|---|---|---|
| BEETLE | DEER | SQUIRREL |
| BIRCH | IVY | TOADSTOOL |
| CLEARING | MUSHROOM | TRUNK |
| CROW | OWL | WOODPECKER |

# Gentle

## 80: INSECTS

Find all of these words in the grid.
Look up, down, and across.
Words can run backward as well as forward.

```
N E A R G I W R A E J Y
O M O S P K T S U C O L
T O F F O M R L M J D F
I S T E N R O H L Z E N
A Q E R S A U E I Z L O
E U K O V G T A V I T G
V I C E N T I P E D E A
W T I K L N A P E F E R
A O R L F S A M W M B D
S E C H L T E R M I T E
P E H K E E H E R B A U
N E A M A T E R M T E A
```

| | | |
|---|---|---|
| BEETLE | EARWIG | MOSQUITO |
| CENTIPEDE | FLEA | TERMITE |
| CRICKET | HORNET | WASP |
| DRAGONFLY | LOCUST | WEEVIL |

# Gentle

## 81: COSTUME PARTY

Find all of these words in the grid.
Look up, down, and across.
Words can run backward as well as forward.

```
I A R Y A H C T I W L B
E T A R I P A R A T E S
Y R A R A S A T W W E S
E G T U A N O R T S A E
F A I R N G E L E C T C
L E R E G W T V M A M N
O F E O E I H E D R E I
Y T A H L Z G E H E R R
G E N I E A I R K C O P
M I E B A R N D C R E A
F A I R Y D K E W O K R
T O B O R R C L O W N E
```

ANGEL            GENIE            ROBOT

ASTRONAUT        KNIGHT           SCARECROW

CLOWN            PIRATE           WITCH

FAIRY            PRINCESS         WIZARD

# Gentle

## 82: THE SIMPSONS

Find all of these words in the grid.
Look up, down, and across.
Words can run backward as well as forward.

```
M D S M I T H E R S U K
I F L D N O M A R G E R
L S E D E Y R S K O S U
H E N G L T E I I J M S
E Y N U S S J L S E W Y
D M Y E O U C O S G H R
A O T S N R U B R M T F
T U R J H K I M U N Y A
A R A J I M E I B R R E
R G B W A U P J C K W I
E O D E S U O H L I M E
N I T R A M G E L E I S
```

| BART | LISA | MR BURNS |
| JIMBO | MARGE | NELSON |
| KRUSTY | MARTIN | SEYMOUR |
| LENNY | MILHOUSE | SMITHERS |

# Gentle

## 83: THINGS THAT GO ROUND

Find all of these words in the grid.
Look up, down, and across.
Words can run backward as well as forward.

```
L L R O T O R O W A R A
O L L I M D N I W H E T
O I J M E W T S S T F H
P R O P E L L E R R S Y
L D E F E S A C A A A G
R O G J T F I P C E T E
I J O Y E R U W I E E E
H E K N M E C H N H L E
W B A M O V I I G T L E
E Y R O C D E S C F I F
H L T O N U R K A N T N
B E U N E R A Y R W E D
```

| COMET | PROPELLER | THE EARTH |
|-------|-----------|-----------|
| DRILL | RACING CAR | WHIRLPOOL |
| GO-KART | ROTOR | WHISK |
| MOON | SATELLITE | WINDMILL |

## 84: PEOPLE WHO WRITE

Find all of these words in the grid.
Look up, down, and across.
Words can run backward as well as forward.

```
T S I L E V O N E R S A
B H A S Y E H O E N X K
G E D I T O R C L E R K
C R A T H O R A A F N T
T E A C H E R R G E L N
E P R O F E S S O R K E
O O U R E S O P M O C D
P R A O T S I R A I D U
Y T F H E L E E A N D T
E E A T O R E S A B B S
S R J U N E V E L I S T
E H N A I R O T S I H J
```

| | | |
|---|---|---|
| AUTHOR | EDITOR | PROFESSOR |
| CLERK | HISTORIAN | REPORTER |
| COMPOSER | NOVELIST | STUDENT |
| DIARIST | POET | TEACHER |

# Gentle

## 85: ANCIENT EGYPT

Find all of these words in the grid.
Look up, down, and across.
Words can run backward as well as forward.

```
A R N A Y M M U M A G E
R O U A R S P H I N X S
T A M T E A P L E D S U
A M A N F L J D G I W R
P Y H P Y R A M I D S Y
O N K V F B N P D N A P
E I N B M O T H G A Z A
L L A G B A R A C S J P
C E T Q M P Y R M A R I
D F U U E V I A Z I G O
Y P T H V A F O V A Z Z
S E L P M E T H W U R E
```

| | | |
|---|---|---|
| CLEOPATRA | PAPYRUS | SPHINX |
| GIZA | PHARAOH | TEMPLES |
| MUMMY | PYRAMID | TOMB |
| NILE | SCARAB | TUTANKHAMUN |

## 86: DELICIOUS CHOCOLATE

Find all of these words in the grid.
Look up, down, and across.
Words can run backward as well as forward.

```
K C H O C A C O H I S Y
G O H C R E G B A E C O
V C Y E N G G E O Y O H
U O V K E S E S W E E T
M A L A M M R M A S P F
C R U C A O E O E J Q A
H E H C E O T O C I W W
I C N A R A S T U C H R
C L E N C E A H A E I D
E A U D E J E R S S T A
A I L Y C V K E B F E R
M R G N I K N I R D F K
```

| CAKE | DRINKING | SAUCE |
|------|----------|-------|
| CANDY | EASTER EGG | SMOOTH |
| COCOA | ECLAIR | SWEET |
| DARK | ICE CREAM | WHITE |

# Gentle

## 87: SWIMMING POOL

Find all of these words in the grid.
Look up, down, and across.
Words can run backward as well as forward.

```
S K D U H G P W D F W S
P I R V H N E A N L O H
L M A B L I M K E U R A
A S U A A D E A P M M L
S G G T H A D V E E Q L
H P E H O W J R E T A W
M T F A Y I B H D B V I
W H I S T L E Q D K T E
A I L F L W A R C L P N
N S H A L L O W E N D H
B D I V I N G B O A R D
G N I H T A B E C O L D
```

| BATHING | DIVING BOARD | SPLASH |
|---------|--------------|--------|
| COLD | FLUME | WADING |
| CRAWL | LIFEGUARD | WATER |
| DEEP END | SHALLOW END | WHISTLE |

# Gentle

## 88: ON THE FARM

Find all of these words in the grid.
Look up, down, and across.
Words can run backward as well as forward.

```
F A R M W K E A D O C O
O U T I O D S I K F P S
T E E R D R O T A N W J
R D I B A A S D L E I F
O I F R E Y E S I D P O
U T T E M M A R L E J R
G C R M E R U T S A P C
H H A K P A B A R N S H
S E C N E F R I H K P A
C S T J O R C H A O O R
K O O F E R A N S Z R D
W O R C E R A C S T C M
```

| | | |
|---|---|---|
| BARNS | FENCES | PASTURE |
| CROPS | FIELDS | SCARECROW |
| DITCHES | MEADOW | TRACTOR |
| FARMYARD | ORCHARD | TROUGHS |

# Gentle

## 89: BUSY BEES

Find all of these words in the grid.
Look up, down, and across.
Words can run backward as well as forward.

```
L H P Y J A M H O N E Y
O S T L B P E A X W A X
Y R N L N P O L L E N W
A E E E E U H G M H U T
R W V J E E E U Q W E M
Y O G L U R Y Y K O N O
E L N A Q L N H E R O N
L F I Y U E O I V K R I
E K Z O E M L V A E D S
M I Z R N O O E B R U E
A B U R A T C E N A C R
U I B V R E R N C B A N
```

BUZZING          HIVE           QUEEN

COLONY           HONEY          ROYAL JELLY

DRONE            NECTAR         WAX

FLOWERS          POLLEN         WORKER

# Gentle

## 90: CAPITAL CITIES OF THE WORLD

Find all of these words in the grid.
Look up, down, and across.
Words can run backward as well as forward.

```
N E G A H N E P O C B V
F U N S T O C K H O L M
D I R D A M S T O C K S
L Z S I R A P D E S A J
O K I V A J K Y E R A E
N E L O N D N V X H T P
D O C O R E N H A G H M
O S R M O S C O W V E E
N L A N O T T A W A N S
Z O R E Y J K A V W S T
C D N O T G N I H S A W
W I N I K N I S L E H C
```

| | | |
|---|---|---|
| ATHENS | MADRID | PARIS |
| COPENHAGEN | MOSCOW | REYKJAVIK |
| HELSINKI | OSLO | STOCKHOLM |
| LONDON | OTTAWA | WASHINGTON DC |

# Gentle

## 91: FELINE FRIENDS

Find all of these words in the grid.
Look up, down, and across.
Words can run backward as well as forward.

```
B R U S H I N G O L E T
S P L A Y F U L E T Y S
R F P E S R Y Z U E T E
E T G X F I P I E K I Z
K F R C O L L A R S S J
S L O X O R F O F A O P
I R O C D U T E A B I U
H K M A B B E A R T R R
W F I T O D A R H A U R
K E N N W S W A L C C I
P F G I L C U T E L B N
E I A P B C C L A U V G
```

| | | |
|---|---|---|
| BASKET | COLLAR | GROOMING |
| BRUSHING | CURIOSITY | PLAYFUL |
| CATNIP | CUTE | PURRING |
| CLAWS | FOOD BOWL | WHISKERS |

# Gentle

## 92: ROOM INSIDE

Find all of these words in the grid.
Look up, down, and across.
Words can run backward as well as forward.

```
B E E Y R O O M E F H A
B E D R O O M K A R O Y
Y L N E E O F F I C E D
W O E S P A N T R Y I K
Y U H R B H R A L L E C
D N C U B A T H R O O M
U G T N V L A T T I C E
T E I T S L I R A L A X
S T K I H W R E L W Q Q
E K L L E A F R E A K D
E V E R R Y M A L Y H D
A G L R T N E M E S A B
```

ATTIC            CELLAR          NURSERY

BASEMENT         HALLWAY         OFFICE

BATHROOM         KITCHEN         PANTRY

BEDROOM          LOUNGE          STUDY

# Gentle

## 93: MARINE LIFE

Find all of these words in the grid.
Look up, down, and across.
Words can run backward as well as forward.

```
P L O K M U S P W G D J
E L E R V P W H A L E O
T S K A T U R T L E V Y
S E G H E L K U R A E R
T A D S K O C T U L E E
A L R L O B S H S E Y I
R I E H S I F Y L L E J
F O T O C T O P U S I G
I N S W B I J S Q U I D
S E B S P M I R H S H I
H D O L P H I N E F C V
B N L E N B D O L P H O
```

DOLPHIN          SEA LION          STARFISH

JELLYFISH        SHARK             TURTLE

LOBSTER          SHRIMP            WALRUS

OCTOPUS          SQUID             WHALE

## 94: TELEVISION

Find all of these words in the grid.
Look up, down, and across.
Words can run backward as well as forward.

```
R O E P I D O R E M C U
I N T E R V I E W V A T
P L D C H A N N E L R N
R E P I S O D E D A T E
E P C O M E D Y N L O K
S N T E L E R T U O O S
E S L A R Y G L O I N W
N C A R E M A C S D S E
T R B A T U L P D U S N
E E D E A S E H U T H F
R E G E S I Y L F S Q D
W N C A P C W I L D L K
```

| | | |
|---|---|---|
| CAMERA | EPISODE | PRESENTER |
| CARTOONS | INTERVIEW | SCREEN |
| CHANNEL | MUSIC | SOUND |
| COMEDY | NEWS | STUDIO |

# Gentle

## 95: GEOGRAPHICAL FEATURES

Find all of these words in the grid.
Look up, down, and across.
Words can run backward as well as forward.

```
S P E R A E O S I A E T
A P F E I W N O Y N A C
I M U I Z M A E T B W N
D A G C P O C T F E D A
V W O A E U L E O E E M
A S R L B N O R A N S S
L T G G A T V E G W E L
L R E E D A A U C M R O
E A E E O I R E O G T C
Y L O A D N A L S I G E
N C R O N L I F A S A A
H C A E B R I V E R J N
```

BEACH          GORGE          RIVER

CANYON         ISLAND         SWAMP

DESERT         MOUNTAIN       VALLEY

GLACIER        OCEAN          VOLCANO

# Gentle

## 96: THINGS THAT CAN BE HUNG

Find all of these words in the grid.
Look up, down, and across.
Words can run backward as well as forward.

```
K C O L C L L A W E R A
G A N O T I C E C G S H
M C H O T V R O R R I M
R O C A L E N D A R G X
I L E F E A N E A I N T
E C E K C O M M A H Z N
U L R E I L E D N A H C
Y O O D A T S H E L F F
T T D R B Y L E I S D L
E H J T I A R T R O P A
I E M I P N E S U U W G
M S C B L D P O S T E R
```

| | | |
|---|---|---|
| CALENDAR | HAMMOCK | POSTER |
| CHANDELIER | MIRROR | SHELF |
| CLOTHES | NOTICE | SIGN |
| FLAG | PORTRAIT | WALL CLOCK |

# Gentle

## 97: FEELING ADVENTUROUS

Find all of these words in the grid.
Look up, down, and across.
Words can run backward as well as forward.

```
T H R I L L I N G S P D
P E R Y Y K C U L P Y A
S W I S H A R A T O S R
U G E Y A H E R O I C I
O N S S E L R A E F S N
E I L C R I S P I R P G
G T L B K E V A R B I L
A I O O M Y E R T A R B
R C A L E K E D N A I R
U X D D E S B S K P T E
O E H X I I M N A X E L
C U N A F R A I D Y D T
```

| | | |
|---|---|---|
| BOLD | EXCITING | RISKY |
| BRAVE | FEARLESS | SPIRITED |
| COURAGEOUS | HEROIC | THRILLING |
| DARING | PLUCKY | UNAFRAID |

# Gentle

## 98: ROUND OBJECTS

Find all of these words in the grid.
Look up, down, and across.
Words can run backward as well as forward.

```
E E B S I R F S U W X O
E R M N X D R P O P K V
R W H E E A C H M O O N
Y T U K B E N E C E C P
C T A R E R T R T G J V
I P I O F R Y E C N N N
R L M R G C O O K I E L
C A E A Y P P E A R L D
L N I N O R I N A S A I
E E J G B U B B L E N M
M T T E B U T T O N W R
P A U W H E E L U N A A
```

| | | |
|---|---|---|
| BUBBLE | FRISBEE | PLANET |
| BUTTON | MOON | RING |
| CIRCLE | ORANGE | SPHERE |
| COOKIE | PEARL | WHEEL |

# Gentle

## 99: LORD OF THE RINGS

Find all of these words in the grid.
Look up, down, and across.
Words can run backward as well as forward.

```
F L E R O D R O M G M W
U R F N G A N D F A L T
O D O R F F L A D N A G
E N O Y T N E V E L E G
M F M G R A R A G O R N
E C C E O J M E H A D U
R O E R L C E N O G L G
I M I W L E J L B C Q U
A M U L L O G A B L I B
D W E R Y R C W I O C L
O N A A T C S N T L R U
C B L A O S O B L I B A
```

| ARAGORN | FRODO | MERIADOC |
|---|---|---|
| BILBO | GANDALF | MORDOR |
| ELEVENTY-ONE | GOLLUM | ORCS |
| ELF | HOBBIT | TROLL |

# Gentle

## 100: TREASURE ISLAND

Find all of these words in the grid.
Look up, down, and across.
Words can run backward as well as forward.

```
C A B I N B O Y Y T L X
H C D N N U G N E B O F
E K N E G A O H N E U L
T I A R E V D E W N N I
S R L U V E H S A G X N
Y C S S M T U D L O V T
O O I A E L I V E S E Y
H M R E R E G A R E I R
O P K R B E D Z T M I I
H A Z T O R R A P N Y L
O S J I M H A W K I N S
E S H I S P A N I O L A
```

BEN GUNN          HISPANIOLA        PARROT

CABIN BOY         ISLAND            TREASURE

COMPASS           JIM HAWKINS       TRELAWNEY

FLINT             LIVESEY           YO HO HO

# Gentle

**101**: TREES

Find all of these words in the grid.
Look up, down, and across.
Words can run backward as well as forward.

```
T W I L L O W O L L O A
U H J B E E C H L S A S
N I F C A V E C A U S Y
T C E D A R K I R O E C
S K H N I F E D C S E A
E O A P H U H P H S L M
H R Z R E S T O P H P O
C Y E B O I S A K C A R
O M L A P E T A D R M E
N I F E R A T I N I Y T
T I I N B E L L C B M T
G L E U C A L Y P T U S
```

| | | |
|---|---|---|
| BEECH | DATE PALM | LARCH |
| BIRCH | EUCALYPTUS | MAPLE |
| CEDAR | HAZEL | SYCAMORE |
| CHESTNUT | HICKORY | WILLOW |

# Gentle

## 102: COUNTRIES OF SOUTH AMERICA

Find all of these words in the grid.
Look up, down, and across.
Words can run backward as well as forward.

```
V U E M A N I R U S B Z
E T O G C O L O M B I A
N T U U R U G U A Y M C
E P A F G U Y A N A J H
R O D A U C E R N E B I
F V O L I V S G P S O L
A L E U Z E N E V A L E
R T B P E R U N U C I I
U N U J N T R T W H V L
Y P E R A N F I P I I A
C B R A Z I L N I L A M
R Y A U G A R A P T A K
```

| | | |
|---|---|---|
| ARGENTINA | COLOMBIA | PERU |
| BOLIVIA | ECUADOR | SURINAME |
| BRAZIL | GUYANA | URUGUAY |
| CHILE | PARAGUAY | VENEZUELA |

# Gentle

103: **THINGS YOU CAN PEEL**

Find all of these words in the grid.
Look up, down, and across.
Words can run backward as well as forward.

```
K R A B E E R T S L I M
O R E N E T O M A T O P
E G N A R O N I O N N M
V M O O R H S U M R I I
G Z E L P P A E G E S R
A E C L M G Y T G P P H
R M L E B A L N E G D S
O E M H O N H I D K E S
N D T S P O T A T O F E
D S E G C T D P G U I V
I O E G C A R R O T O I
S F Z E H M H A P I Y E
```

APPLE            MUSHROOM         POTATO

CARROT           ONION            SHRIMP

EGGSHELL         ORANGE           TOMATO

LABEL            PAINT            TREE BARK

# Gentle

## 104: CARNIVAL

Find all of these words in the grid.
Look up, down, and across.
Words can run backward as well as forward.

```
S J U G G L E R S E R U
E L I M E S R E C N A D
T E G D I S P L A Y V S
T S V S T R E E M T S A
E E R C O S T U M E S R
R S T A B O R C A D N G
O R S L Y O D I J A H I
J O N F D J R J E R U D
A H W L E V U F E A V R
M T O A A S M P E P S A
M F L G E E S H E P B M
Y A C S P A R I N A T E
```

| ACROBATS | DISPLAY | JUGGLERS |
|----------|---------|----------|
| CLOWNS | DRUMS | MAJORETTES |
| COSTUMES | FLAGS | MARDI GRAS |
| DANCERS | HORSES | PARADE |

# Gentle

## 105: WATER

Find all of these words in the grid.
Look up, down, and across.
Words can run backward as well as forward.

```
V O S T R E E M O A S I
E D F A L L I D E O B S
T R A I N F A L L W D N
N E C T R I D E K H Y I
E S J B R O O K C I R A
R Y C E X W D F I R A T
R E O H A A L U R L U N
U G A S T V A Y T P T U
C Y S N U E N M H O S O
J E I U F S A E E O E F
B A S G T O C H R L M E
L U W A T E R F A L L N
```

| | | |
|---|---|---|
| BROOK | FOUNTAIN | TRICKLE |
| CANAL | GEYSER | WATERFALL |
| CURRENT | OASIS | WAVES |
| ESTUARY | RAINFALL | WHIRLPOOL |

## Gentle

### 106: SLUMBER PARTY

Find all of these words in the grid.
Look up, down, and across.
Words can run backward as well as forward.

```
M H S I N G I N G B P H
B E D R O O M Y T B A U
G A M E R I T A T I O D
S C A G F R I E N D S S
E H G N I Y A L P T R A
I A C I C Q F E D A L I
R T I L Y S W O L L I P
O T S G N J E W W K U C
T I U G S E M A G I L A
S N M I C E S T E N M K
K G V G O I P E R G N E
W F G E M E S L E P L S
```

| | | |
|---|---|---|
| BEDROOM | GAMES | PLAYING |
| CAKES | GIGGLING | SINGING |
| CHATTING | MUSIC | STORIES |
| FRIENDS | PILLOWS | TALKING |

# Gentle

## 107: HOBBIES AND PASTIMES

Find all of these words in the grid.
Look up, down, and across.
Words can run backward as well as forward.

```
G A M E O P O T T W E R
N I N H E J I G S A W S
I S I N G I N G F L P G
W T E P F S P B G K E N
O P O T T E R Y N I G I
R G N L G L M A I N N I
V N A E N Z A P D G I K
Y I C S I Z E W I R T S
I D E A K U L L A I N B
L I E Z I P E G R T I J
T R A B H D V B B E A N
G N I W E S Q P U S P Z
```

| BRAIDING | POTTERY | SEWING |
| HIKING | PUZZLES | SINGING |
| JIGSAWS | RIDING | SKIING |
| PAINTING | ROWING | WALKING |

## Gentle

**108: ALICE IN WONDERLAND**

Find all of these words in the grid.
Look up, down, and across.
Words can run backward as well as forward.

```
S S E H C U D O F W E D
W A L S U R O A L A E E
V E N D I N A H C L A N
E R R S E M K N I R D Y
Y T R A P A E T K U D E
E R A H H C R A M S S A
V E L C A L I C E A T E
E G C A R P E N T E R M
I A C F C R O Q U E T N
D R E T T A H D A M D L
T E A P A R T E A T M E
V C A T E R P I L L A R
```

| | | |
|---|---|---|
| ALICE | DINAH | MAD HATTER |
| CARPENTER | DRINK ME | MARCH HARE |
| CATERPILLAR | DUCHESS | TEA PARTY |
| CROQUET | EAT ME | WALRUS |

# Gentle

## 109: HERBS AND SPICES

Find all of these words in the grid.
Look up, down, and across.
Words can run backward as well as forward.

```
P A R E S E L Y R O S A
E L I M O M A C C C O R
O J A I O P A P R I K A
G E N G E R S R H N N N
S P A R S L E Y H N G G
R E G N I G B O R A G E
E M Y H T A S O T M B L
D M C I N E M I N O A I
R I S E M A R Y C N S C
C O R I A N D E R P I A
P E P R E S A G E E L E
V E Y R A M E S O R L E
```

| | | |
|---|---|---|
| ANGELICA | CINNAMON | PARSLEY |
| BASIL | CORIANDER | ROSEMARY |
| BORAGE | GINGER | SAGE |
| CAMOMILE | PAPRIKA | THYME |

# Gentle

## 110: FLYING MACHINES

Find all of these words in the grid.
Look up, down, and across.
Words can run backward as well as forward.

```
R F R D N A P L I N E E
E M E A O B M E C A G N
T I D D O P I A H E E A
P C I S L B L R O N S L
O R L R L A B A P A M P
C O G O A S T E P L V I
I L W W B A C K E P P R
L I S P A C E C R A F T
E G E N O R D O O E O I
H H S H U T T L E S K K
H T Z V E R O C K E T T
E D B R E L L O O N A O
```

| | | |
|---|---|---|
| BALLOON | GLIDER | SEAPLANE |
| BLIMP | HELICOPTER | SHUTTLE |
| CHOPPER | MICROLIGHT | SPACECRAFT |
| DRONE | ROCKET | TRIPLANE |

# Gentle

**111**: SPORTS VENUES

Find all of these words in the grid.
Look up, down, and across.
Words can run backward as well as forward.

```
P G T R I P R O T I S A
S Y D N U O R G E D A X
K M S P E E D W A Y N S
I N N E M O R D O L E V
J A C A I I R L A J R Q
U S O C S E R A N O A H
M I U S T A D U E M E A
P U R R I N K I P O O L
K M S M E R I A N E A U
T G E E G R A R A N G E
O G Y M E N A S T E R U
F I E L D C I R C U I T
```

| | | |
|---|---|---|
| ARENA | GROUND | RINK |
| CIRCUIT | GYMNASIUM | SKI JUMP |
| COURSE | POOL | SPEEDWAY |
| FIELD | RANGE | VELODROME |

# Gentle

## 112: COUNTRIES OF AFRICA

Find all of these words in the grid.
Look up, down, and across.
Words can run backward as well as forward.

```
O R I S B O T S W A N A
K N A L G E R I A S S A
E A H Z I M B A B W E D
N M D A M I B I A T Z N
Y I A B I T S W A R V A
A B A D N A G U L V Y W
A I P O I H T E I G W R
L A O G A E T H I A P C
I W T U N I S I A I K O
B D O M N I M A L A W I
Y R R E A N D A L A N D
A L O G N A A E V A H H
```

| ALGERIA | KENYA | RWANDA |
|---------|-------|--------|
| ANGOLA | LIBYA | TUNISIA |
| BOTSWANA | MALAWI | UGANDA |
| ETHIOPIA | NAMIBIA | ZIMBABWE |

# Gentle

## 113: ALL TOGETHER

Find all of these words in the grid.
Look up, down, and across.
Words can run backward as well as forward.

```
T A C R O W D Y G T R E
E E E D T V R H N R A R
E Y W D R E H S A B G E
R F A H H I C H G K R C
E A S D E R R I M B O M
T P A C E D E L D N U B
S M A E T W W B N T P G
U H V F L O C K G E M A
L I V O S K C A T S C G
C H C T U L C G E A S E
R E V E N I T U R A L E
K A M I L E C S W A R M
```

| | | |
|---|---|---|
| BUNDLE | CROWD | HERD |
| CLUSTER | FLOCK | STACK |
| CLUTCH | GANG | SWARM |
| CREW | GROUP | TEAM |

# Challenging

## 114: THINGS WITH STRINGS

Find all of these words in the grid.
Look up, down, across, and diagonally.
Words can run backward as well as forward.

```
V E R I N I L E B E L A
E T I K J E P A L E U C
R E P S C I N U Y O Y O
T F F R D B N E P G Y Q
Z G A I B A N J O P D U
R P A U D O X I V T E X
K A O T R D S Y L L I T
E D T P T D L S E O S A
D W A I V F L E E J I E
S U M M U O I Z A M N V
L E B A L G E G A R E N
W I N D C H I M E S W E
```

| | | |
|---|---|---|
| APRON | GUITAR | PUPPET |
| BANJO | KITE | VIOLIN |
| FIDDLE | LABEL | WIND CHIMES |
| GIFT TAG | PARCEL | YO-YO |

# Challenging

## 115: STATES OF AMERICA

Find all of these words in the grid.
Look up, down, across, and diagonally.
Words can run backward as well as forward.

```
E X A S M A I M N N A S
N D N A L Y R A M M M A
I I A Y F W G K A A I S
S U E T A I W B K K S S
N W I S H U A A V S S A
O O K C F L E T A A O X
C B I I A W A H S L U E
S M W Y O M I N G A R T
I N I M A N A J O R I C
W G E Y O K L A H O M A
C O L O R A D O M N H G
C E V A Y K E N S I S E
```

| ALABAMA | HAWAII | OKLAHOMA |
|---------|--------|----------|
| ALASKA | MARYLAND | TEXAS |
| ARKANSAS | MICHIGAN | WISCONSIN |
| COLORADO | MISSOURI | WYOMING |

# Challenging

## 116: HARVEST TIME

Find all of these words in the grid.
Look up, down, across, and diagonally.
Words can run backward as well as forward.

```
Y F A R M Y A R D V G Y
H A R V E R E R H N G T
S O S N A P Y B I T N N
E T U Z N I U N U R I E
A U N E N E E U E A T L
U K S G E P V L N C T P
I P H V I E I A H T U B
G D I R T A F A Y O C A
E C N C R V D R B R F L
M D E T K E S R U I T E
W H E A T E I N I I E S
O H T R A C R B E L T S
```

BALES          FRUIT          SUNSHINE

CUTTING        PICKER         TRACTOR

DRYING         PLENTY         TRAILER

FARMYARD       RIPENING       WHEAT

# Challenging

## 117: HALLOWEEN

Find all of these words in the grid.
Look up, down, across, and diagonally.
Words can run backward as well as forward.

```
S E I T R A P S W Y K S
G H O S E V E Y I T C E
O C S J Z M D G S H I H
R E T P U J N M I G T C
F S E T E I K A T I S T
H V S E T L F S I N M I
N O Y N E S L K O D O W
C S U L T H P S R I O K
C A N D L E S A R M R D
H V E W I C H E S P B J
T R I C K O R T R E A T
Q P U M P K I N L A M P
```

| BROOMSTICK | HAUNTING | PUMPKIN LAMP |
|---|---|---|
| CANDLES | MASKS | SPELLS |
| COSTUMES | MIDNIGHT | TRICK OR TREAT |
| FROGS | PARTIES | WITCHES |

# Challenging

## 118: ROBIN HOOD

Find all of these words in the grid.
Look up, down, across, and diagonally.
Words can run backward as well as forward.

```
N M E R R Y M E N D T M
A H P H A R S I O C A S
I S O I E R A O J H H H
R T E J Y A W V G Z H E
A E S T E R R N V T C R
M K R E E L I C Y B A I
D I E H R T T M H Y I F
I N S R T O T T C E E F
A G B O A M F D I F R A
M F N G A Z O U T L A W
K C U T R A I R F A R S
U N H O J G N I K U A E
```

ARCHER            LITTLE JOHN        NOTTINGHAM

FOREST            MAID MARIAN        OUTLAW

FRIAR TUCK        MERRY MEN          SHERIFF

KING JOHN         MYTH               SHERWOOD

# Challenging

## 119: FRUITS AND NUTS

Find all of these words in the grid.
Look up, down, across, and diagonally.
Words can run backward as well as forward.

```
O R A N P L E M O N N C
M W T E H A Z E R E W E
O C A U I B A N A F G V
N C Y E N T E T N G O I
H O G E A L U Y A N R L
A R B E P R A N N M O O
G A Y R R E B W A R T S
C N L Y I F C D B E Z F
H G B E C H E R R Y P D
E E L A O F U A P P E L
R N M U T A L M O N D W
Y G P I S T A C H I O I
```

ALMOND          LEMON          PEANUT

APRICOT         OLIVE          PISTACHIO

BANANA          ORANGE         STRAWBERRY

CHERRY          PEACH          WALNUT

# Challenging

## 120: A GAME OF CHESS

Find all of these words in the grid.
Look up, down, across, and diagonally.
Words can run backward as well as forward.

```
L C K N E E N K I N L P
A M F K N I G H T E O B
E E O B E P A S P H C O
B T D V V O S F S I U A
E A U W E F P I R E O R
T M G R R S B R O O G D
I K B O A D W H I T A N
H C A S T L E B K I N G
W E Q U E E N J V A N B
A H K O O W I K C A L B
S C V E A T E M Y U Q U
N A W P L I W C K O O R
```

| BISHOP | CHECKMATE | PAWN |
|--------|-----------|------|
| BLACK | KING | QUEEN |
| BOARD | KNIGHT | ROOK |
| CASTLE | MOVES | WHITE |

# Challenging

## 121: SPORTS EQUIPMENT

Find all of these words in the grid.
Look up, down, across, and diagonally.
Words can run backward as well as forward.

```
P L F L L E B O J A V U
L E E H L B E A R S I G
I K B S A A V E B I O N
T R B A S E B A L L X E
I O E C L A G T F V F L
N N V I S C S C O B B D
P S N K U H L E G O S R
A H E A P U U L T S F U
D T M R B K O I V A N H
D G S E N V P A K E K S
L L A B E P N O T A B S
E D T S T O P S N E R S
```

| BASEBALL | GLOVES | NETS |
| --- | --- | --- |
| BASKET | GOLF CLUB | PADDLE |
| BATON | HURDLE | SKATES |
| FOOTBALL | JAVELIN | SNORKEL |

# Challenging

## 122: WILD WEST USA

Find all of these words in the grid.
Look up, down, across, and diagonally.
Words can run backward as well as forward.

```
L I V P U D N U O R W N
P H A R E T A B L C A P
E S S E L O N D O P G L
W U N W K L A S E E O R
T R E C A T T L E F N U
L D E S T L X A F H S S
Y L S V O M T I L E T T
O O K F Y E R U R U E L
B G E F B E D A O E T E
W D E D H U N O C J S R
O W H S I C U P R T O M
C H I D H A N C H A N E
```

| CATTLE | OUTLAWS | RUSTLER |
| COWBOY | RANCH | SHERIFF |
| GOLD RUSH | RODEO | STETSON |
| LASSO | ROUND-UP | WAGONS |

# Challenging

## 123: STRONG SMELLS

Find all of these words in the grid.
Look up, down, across, and diagonally.
Words can run backward as well as forward.

```
B A C O F F C O F F E E
W A B A D E G G S C M W
A M A A R E D N E V A L
R A T A N G A R L I C E
M N E N R A M A N A S M
B N R A P O N C R T K O
R I E C I N N A M O N N
E C I R A M G Y U L E P
A P E P P E R M I N T E
D E G E N O S E R L E E
S N O I N O D E I R F L
N Y V H O T C A K E S M
```

| | | |
|---|---|---|
| BAD EGGS | FRIED ONIONS | LEMON PEEL |
| BANANA | GARLIC | PEPPERMINT |
| CINNAMON | HOT CAKES | VINEGAR |
| COFFEE | LAVENDER | WARM BREAD |

## Challenging

### 124: LUMPS AND BUMPS

Find all of these words in the grid.
Look up, down, across, and diagonally.
Words can run backward as well as forward.

```
H U R B E L A H S E V R
S I N A U E T O R H N E
E G L U B W L P U O F T
G A L L O F I P D M E S
N D E R C E G U M S E U
I E G S C D L O B I D L
L E X E N E N L A E P C
L N O I T C E J O R P N
E B M O P E R A L M I D
W F A N T A S F U M E S
S S A M F E A L P M U H
B A K N U H C H E E R E
```

| | | |
|---|---|---|
| BULGE | GROWTH | PIECE |
| CHUNK | HUMP | PIMPLE |
| CLUMP | MASS | PROJECTION |
| CLUSTER | NODULE | SWELLING |

# Challenging

## 125: FUN AT THE FAIR

Find all of these words in the grid.
Look up, down, across, and diagonally.
Words can run backward as well as forward.

```
A R N E Z A M I A S U O
L R T I E M C E W S E H
P E N S A E Y O T F C P
O P E C C R H S G H R P
O O M R L S T S O M O R
H K E A E G U T A L W I
E A T D A T D U S B D Z
M Z I U J O D N R O S E
U S C R G P H O O N H S
S K X E V E R C R E W G
I E E O E M Y O E U A F
C H R I D E S C S I Y E
```

| COCONUTS | HOOP-LA | MUSIC |
| --- | --- | --- |
| CROWDS | HOT DOG | PRIZES |
| EXCITEMENT | ICE CREAM | RIDES |
| GHOST TRAIN | MAZE | SIDESHOWS |

# Challenging

## 126: WILDLIFE OF AUSTRALIA

Find all of these words in the grid.
Look up, down, across, and diagonally.
Words can run backward as well as forward.

```
K A N W P L A T Y P U S
W P L A O A A D I N G O
Y A M T L M B I L B O O
A P L A A S B E T T A R
N T O L F S I A O P N A
D K O Y A V M O T A N G
I A R E C B C A S Z A K
H U A A J I Y G O A N E
C L G R D B D B I L B Y
E I N N C A N E T O A D
Y P A R R U B A K O O K
S B K K E C A H I D N E
```

| | | |
|---|---|---|
| BANDICOOT | ECHIDNA | KOOKABURRA |
| BILBY | GOANNA | PLATYPUS |
| CANE TOAD | KANGAROO | WALLABY |
| DINGO | KOALA | WOMBAT |

# Challenging

## 127: SWEETS AND CANDIES

Find all of these words in the grid.
Look up, down, across, and diagonally.
Words can run backward as well as forward.

```
L S Y L O L L Y P E R T
Y G D C H O C A T I M E
A U N S N E E A D E J L
W B A H N R L R D L E E
S M C H Y O L E M F L F
F U M S C D U E C F L P
O H A O H L N G E U Y O
N K H E U E A R A R B P
D C L E M A R A C T E C
A G A R I S I B O N A O
N A P I Z R A M E P N R
T L O L L I P O P T S N
```

| CANDY | HUMBUGS | NOUGAT |
|-------|---------|--------|
| CARAMEL | JELLY BEANS | POPCORN |
| CHOCOLATE | LOLLIPOP | SHERBET |
| FONDANT | MARZIPAN | TRUFFLE |

# Challenging

### 128: LET'S GO CAMPING

Find all of these words in the grid.
Look up, down, across, and diagonally.
Words can run backward as well as forward.

```
T G E P T E N H D T E L
Y N N L O E A L L S U F
C I E I J L E P I Y E O
Q A T T K I E T F H P G
T R M E F O E S J I O E
U E M P E T O L R G R S
A L K G G M H C U J Y E
I I H N F R C Y G N U K
M A P M A G O E S E G A
F R D G P L E U H W U T
G T E B E N B Y N N P S
C A M P R A S E T D H S
```

| | | |
|---|---|---|
| BLANKET | FIRE | SITE |
| CAMPGROUND | GUY ROPE | STAKES |
| COOKING | POLES | TENT |
| FIELD | RUGS | TRAILER |

## 129: MONTHS OF THE YEAR

Find all of these words in the grid.
Look up, down, across, and diagonally.
Words can run backward as well as forward.

```
Y R A R K D E C E N B G
C R E H E E M N O C T O
D F A S K B L A U N D A
N E Y U E P M R R J O R
O F C Y R N E E T C A O
V M H E A B T G T W H E
E B Y E M S E O D P Y V
M A E E U B B F O X E A
M C V G G E E J U M P S
E O U E R I S R I R G H
N A F E B R U H I W B N
J A N U A R Y L J U L Y
```

| APRIL | JANUARY | MAY |
| AUGUST | JULY | NOVEMBER |
| DECEMBER | JUNE | OCTOBER |
| FEBRUARY | MARCH | SEPTEMBER |

# Challenging

## 130: DESERTS

Find all of these words in the grid.
Look up, down, across, and diagonally.
Words can run backward as well as forward.

```
S Y D N A S E L T T I L
E K F E R E S I A T N P
A V A H A F L E D A H G
A N Z L H E D I I S J O
M F A O A E N B B R W B
N O T I S H A D O Y D I
O S J U B R A L S Y A A
S O R A A U U R Y E H N
P N R L V E N V I A P O
M D F A D E T N I A P N
I N O O I A T A C A M A
S I R O G I B S O N M T
```

| | | |
|---|---|---|
| ARABIAN | KALAHARI | NUBIAN |
| ATACAMA | LIBYAN | PAINTED |
| GIBSON | LITTLE SANDY | SAHARA |
| GOBI | MOJAVE | SIMPSON |

# Challenging

## 131: LANGUAGES

Find all of these words in the grid.
Look up, down, across, and diagonally.
Words can run backward as well as forward.

```
I  T  E  R  S  P  A  N  I  S  H  E
H  A  I  T  A  L  I  A  N  U  G  N
S  B  J  A  P  A  N  E  S  E  B  G
I  N  D  K  C  H  I  A  H  H  M  L
N  A  O  E  G  H  F  S  N  W  P  I
N  I  E  O  H  S  I  D  E  W  S  S
I  G  R  B  T  N  K  N  H  E  A  H
F  E  A  R  A  B  I  C  E  W  Y  E
A  W  T  D  F  L  N  R  G  S  U  R
L  R  O  M  E  E  A  R  A  U  E  I
N  O  Y  U  R  U  S  S  I  A  N  T
K  N  G  F  T  C  I  S  H  O  R  N
```

| ARABIC | FINNISH | NORWEGIAN |
|--------|---------|-----------|
| CHINESE | FRENCH | RUSSIAN |
| DANISH | ITALIAN | SPANISH |
| ENGLISH | JAPANESE | SWEDISH |

# Challenging

## 132: SIGNS

Find all of these words in the grid.
Look up, down, across, and diagonally.
Words can run backward as well as forward.

```
E W E T E Y C C T L E T
S P A R Y L P U T A E C
A F N Y O P O I N T O N
E L O S F Y B E I I Y T
L V E R A I S D A P I F
P D N W S B R R P S E E
T E T R S A J E T O F L
E U R E C R L U E H E N
I T Y P H G Z E W X F R
U L T U O P E E K G I U
Q Y L N O F F A T S Y T
R E T H L S T U R N E D
```

CLOSED            KEEP OUT            STAFF ONLY

FIRE EXIT         NO ENTRY            TURN LEFT

FOR SALE          QUIET PLEASE        WAY OUT

HOSPITAL          SCHOOL              WET PAINT

# Challenging

## 133: IN THE SHED

Find all of these words in the grid.
Look up, down, across, and diagonally.
Words can run backward as well as forward.

```
E K D E W H E E L H R C
T B W L A W N M O W E R
E I O O J M B E I V D S
I C R S E S G U L F D D
S Y R E O V S N C L A X
U C A R A K E S A K L L
T L B P V R F E N B E S
R E L E N O S S E A P T
O T E T R S P L K O O W
W O E K M T A E E C N E
E R H J E R D U R I A V
L A W S S R E D I P S S
```

BICYCLE            LAWNMOWER          SPADE

BUCKET             OILCAN             SPIDERS

FORK               RAKE               TROWEL

LADDER             SACKS              WHEELBARROW

# Challenging

### 134: INDOOR GAMES

Find all of these words in the grid.
Look up, down, across, and diagonally.
Words can run backward as well as forward.

```
K G N I L W O B E M B F
L E J U S T Y W O R A I
E T E E G P J N C H E S
T S Y S S O O O K Y O C
M M R I D P S Q U A S H
S A S E O N I M O D E A
E C H L K V A L A E Y R
L H Y J J C O E O D A A
B E B C O B E O D C E D
R S I M B N I H G I N E
A S P A D Y G D C L H S
M H E G N O P G N I P F
```

| BOWLING | DOMINOES | MARBLES |
|---------|----------|---------|
| CHARADES | HIDE AND SEEK | MONOPOLY |
| CHECKERS | I SPY | PING-PONG |
| CHESS | MAH-JONGG | SQUASH |

# Challenging

## 135: BIRDS

Find all of these words in the grid.
Look up, down, across, and diagonally.
Words can run backward as well as forward.

```
N O E G I P H B G D O W
C E O R C K C G H L O A
E S O O G J I K N R W A
Y L C S W A R O C A E E
R N G H E D T K W L W M
A O R A F E S H P L E S
N R L H E O O I N P H G
A E E S T O R K U A M M
C A I A M U A H E R O N
O S T E R A C A E R S C
F L A M I N G O H O B E
H G R G N I L R A T S S
```

| CANARY | GOOSE | PIGEON |
| CROW | HERON | STARLING |
| EAGLE | OSTRICH | STORK |
| FLAMINGO | PARROT | SWAN |

# Challenging

## 136: MOONS OF THE SOLAR SYSTEM

Find all of these words in the grid.
Look up, down, across, and diagonally.
Words can run backward as well as forward.

```
H Y P E R I O N L U S A
I M O T S I L L A C O C
A P E R I O S A H D B A
P C E G M E T M E Z O L
E E A A W I H I Y X H Y
T M R N J C M H H T P P
U T T Y V O W A E F V S
S I I M S J K T S D I O
J T L E R F H E N A N L
I A E D J Y A M A R U I
Y N Y E S E O A R I E L
A M A L T H E A R O P A
```

| | | |
|---|---|---|
| AMALTHEA | DEIMOS | MIMAS |
| ARIEL | GANYMEDE | PHOBOS |
| CALLISTO | HYPERION | TETHYS |
| CALYPSO | IAPETUS | TITAN |

# Challenging

## 137: CARTOON CHARACTERS

Find all of these words in the grid.
Look up, down, across, and diagonally.
Words can run backward as well as forward.

```
R R E P E P E L E P E W
E V E L L T O P C A T A
N I H T O U S R O A D E
N E P B S L T I M Y S Y
U D M Y S E I O H C R E
R U S T T T E V E A L P
D D U F R E M L E R E O
A R T G C U E B Y O G P
O D T O D P I W D E Y A
R A G O Y G I W T P S L
E E D F O R L A U G H P
B X S Y L V E S T E R A
```

| | | |
|---|---|---|
| DUMBO | PEPE LE PEW | SYLVESTER |
| ELMER FUDD | PLUTO | TOP CAT |
| GOOFY | POPEYE | TWEETY PIE |
| OLIVE OYL | ROAD RUNNER | YOGI BEAR |

# Challenging

## 138: HARD TO SEE

Find all of these words in the grid.
Look up, down, across, and diagonally.
Words can run backward as well as forward.

```
L D A R E B S E E A L E
E E H U N C L E A R M V
V D F O G G Y U K U G E
E U O M I S E V R N E K
Y O H O X Y T K A R N A
Z L L O R A Y R L J E F
Z C O N C E A L E D A D
U R Y R R U L A M I U G
F S T B H D O L N S K M
I J S E G A L T K A V M
T E I I L R Z Y L I T A
A S M G W K E Y L E U I
```

| BLURRED | DUSKY | HAZY |
| CLOUDED | FAINT | MISTY |
| CONCEALED | FOGGY | MURKY |
| DARK | FUZZY | UNCLEAR |

# Challenging

## 139: FAST FOOD

Find all of these words in the grid.
Look up, down, across, and diagonally.
Words can run backward as well as forward.

```
H E R I D C H I C K E N
S G L U E S E R A E P U
I L D S U H E R S I A P
F C D U H L D A E W I A
A H N E O A U K O R Y R
H E I R L C K Y S B B T
M E V A E L A E D W U Y
P S S S N M L A S E N S
U E L L A R E L G N S N
R L T O M A T O E S A K
R A V I N T E R A S B B
R U B R E T N U O C R A
```

BUNS          FISH          SALAD

CHEESE        MAYO          SAUCES

CHICKEN       MENU          SHAKES

COUNTER       PARTY         TOMATOES

# Challenging

## 140: SHAKE ABOUT

Find all of these words in the grid.
Look up, down, across, and diagonally.
Words can run backward as well as forward.

```
P V E T A T E E T E R J
T U S T E E L W M E G I
E B S T A G G E R E E G
T O D S G R I U T S N S
T U A I U L B A U S Z S
E N J N L Q S I Z V I R
R C E A U L Y P V Q K E
O E F I U T A A S O L D
E L V P B U W R N G K D
W E L I H U S L G S I U
R O C K I S M A L N A J
U T F L I U W P O T S E
```

| BOUNCE | PULSATE | SWAY    |
| BUMP   | QUIVER  | TEETER  |
| JIGGLE | ROCK    | VIBRATE |
| JUDDER | STAGGER | WAGGLE  |

# Challenging

## 141: IN BLACK AND WHITE

Find all of these words in the grid.
Look up, down, across, and diagonally.
Words can run backward as well as forward.

```
E A C H E S S B O A R D
M H E R B S C E A R E I
U D N E W S P A P E R N
G O P N D G N K C D H I
M M I G A B N O A A V U
A I A M J U E Z D L Z G
M N N L K R E T N M C N
A O O S E B I P A A B E
G E K B R M C B P T R P
P S E A N A U P E I S F
I A Y Y P A H R G A P V
E M S E C I D R I N E H
```

| CHESSBOARD | LEMUR | PENGUIN |
|---|---|---|
| DALMATIAN | MAGPIE | PIANO KEYS |
| DICE | NEWSPAPER | SKUNK |
| DOMINOES | PANDA | ZEBRA |

# Challenging

## 142: DANCES

Find all of these words in the grid.
Look up, down, across, and diagonally.
Words can run backward as well as forward.

```
C E F L A M E N C O A B
H V I E R A H A K E G J
A D W A L Z E A K O M I
R H S H I M P Y A L J V
L O G N A D N A F W O E
E I F O X T R O T L E P
S O N J E U A E P I K U
T G F D M W E I G C B C
O N E B Y V A O S C O O
N A A R S H O L S T D N
X T S H P B O H T L E G
U K P O L A H P M Z T A
```

BOOGIE          FLAMENCO        POLKA

CHARLESTON      FOXTROT         RUMBA

CONGA           JIVE            TANGO

FANDANGO        LINDY HOP       WALTZ

# Challenging

## 143: MAKE ME LAUGH

Find all of these words in the grid.
Look up, down, across, and diagonally.
Words can run backward as well as forward.

```
I T G E A M F U N Y A G
P I I P O P C Y S Z S N
U V D C D S K E I D C O
N F T G K F C O O L L N
J I N B A L E I O F E S
S P E R A K I W T L V E
U J J O K E N N D N M N
G C E T E I H D G E A S
Z A Y S N H I E U B E E
T P G G T R K N A R P K
Y E S S F A R A I L E J
J R W N O N E N S E A R
```

| | | |
|---|---|---|
| ANTICS | JEST | PUN |
| CAPER | JOKE | RIDDLE |
| CLOWNING | NONSENSE | SITCOM |
| GAGS | PRANK | TICKLING |

# Challenging

## 144: THE LEGEND OF KING ARTHUR

Find all of these words in the grid.
Look up, down, across, and diagonally.
Words can run backward as well as forward.

```
R U H T R A W M Y K C I
O G A L A H A D R E E K
Y E S R Z R F I P X C N
G E W B T A V E C A A I
A A O S F O N A P V M G
L L R M W D L M N A E H
A R D O R I I E I L L T
T A E A B E S R C O O S
A Y G U E W E L L N T E
C O R C A A R I E G A S
N E L B A T D N U O R L
G U I N E V E R E E A U
```

| ARTHUR | GALAHAD | MERLIN |
| AVALON | GUINEVERE | PENDRAGON |
| CAMELOT | KNIGHTS | ROUND TABLE |
| EXCALIBUR | LANCELOT | SWORD |

# Challenging

## 145: SHARKS

Find all of these words in the grid.
Look up, down, across, and diagonally.
Words can run backward as well as forward.

```
W B C A R P E T M T C F
H L L F T B S C F S A I
I N K A D A M A D O T N
T B K U C S O R A H M A
E J S E R K O E P G J I
M K H B C I T A E H W P
Y E S R U N H I R S J R
C R E W R G H B P I G A
L T L H E S O M A F N W
N O M E L C U C U G A P
P P M A K O N R E O Y E
E E O L K T D L R D I O
```

| ANGEL | DOGFISH | MAKO |
|-------|---------|------|
| BASKING | DUSKY | NURSE |
| BLACK-TIP | GHOST | SMOOTH-HOUND |
| CARPET | LEMON | TOPE |

# Challenging

## 146: MYTHICAL CREATURES

Find all of these words in the grid.
Look up, down, across, and diagonally.
Words can run backward as well as forward.

```
T O N D T E M F D I R T
S F R L M Y A B B U R L
P C O B E I K M A O Y E
O E C H R E L T L J S P
L N I Y M N O L S E M R
C T N S A N D H F O S E
Y A U H I J R G E L S C
C U P M D U E T I E T H
D R W I Y I F B N H V A
V T E Y X Y S A E A I U
P H O E N I X O E L I N
D R A G O N E T N E U G
```

| | | |
|---|---|---|
| CENTAUR | GIANT | PHOENIX |
| CYCLOPS | LEPRECHAUN | PIXIE |
| DRAGON | MERMAID | TROLL |
| FAIRY | MINOTAUR | UNICORN |

# Challenging

**147**: MOUNTAIN RANGES

Find all of these words in the grid.
Look up, down, across, and diagonally.
Words can run backward as well as forward.

```
S C A U C A S U S L R K
E S H E N A N D O A H T
E N K P E L S R S A W E
N S V A E N A C F V H E
E C L X R N Z N A I L A
R I P A E A S M M D E S
Y P T E R B K A N D E S
P M U A H U L O C K R S
J Y A T L A S G R O C L
E L K R Y G E D C A L D
L O O A T N E K Y B M A
F P Y R E N Y A L P S C
```

| | | |
|---|---|---|
| ANDES | HIMALAYA | PYRENEES |
| ATLAS | KARAKORAM | ROCKY |
| CASCADES | OLYMPIC | SHENANDOAH |
| CAUCASUS | PENSACOLA | URALS |

# Challenging

### 148: GREEN THINGS

Find all of these words in the grid.
Look up, down, across, and diagonally.
Words can run backward as well as forward.

```
T G O R F S B E E Y U V
E M E R A L D I G O C C
L I S T I R E L R A Y E
E U S N S E E A E K I L
K D A R E R C W V I R D
D O R B T O E M E E F E
R U G A H L R A V F S E
A I R C Z E Y R I E O N
G R E A V I P T L A S E
O V Z O E G L I O M C N
N K L M T E S A E W P I
E C V M H C A N I P S P
```

| CLOVER | FROG | MARTIAN |
| DRAGON | GRASS | OLIVE |
| EMERALD | LEAVES | PINE NEEDLE |
| FIELDS | LIZARD | SPINACH |

# Challenging

**149**: JOBS

Find all of these words in the grid.
Look up, down, across, and diagonally.
Words can run backward as well as forward.

```
F I T E R E D L I U B W
Y R O S H I S E R S U E
O V L E N T E E S R U N
D R I R I R E A A D H G
Q O P N E A R N I F S I
E M C V E T H R L E E N
I P I T I B N F O D E E
T R A S O C D E R J I E
D E T Y T R A T P N E R
N N T E A C H E R R R B
C A S U A T U M D D A Z
T E G E M E C H A N I C
```

| | | |
|---|---|---|
| ARTIST | DRIVER | NURSE |
| BUILDER | ENGINEER | PILOT |
| CARPENTER | GUARD | SAILOR |
| DOCTOR | MECHANIC | TEACHER |

# Challenging

## 150: ON THE EDGE

Find all of these words in the grid.
Look up, down, across, and diagonally.
Words can run backward as well as forward.

```
P R I P C O R N E R T P
E B E A G O U T L I N E
R A T S E R C E S S N I
I P D R V E D N A R Y H
M C H O L G G D A Y K O
E S R V E L T R B E F R
T E T T L R H I E R E I
E E M I W T S E L V P Z
R A M I U W G T D E D O
T I O O R D E E R P G N
T V M D I B M A R G I N
S T A R U C O R M E N E
```

| | | |
|---|---|---|
| BRIM | LEDGE | OUTLINE |
| CORNER | LIMIT | PERIMETER |
| CREST | MARGIN | RIDGE |
| HORIZON | MOUTH | VERGE |

# Challenging

## 151: TYPES OF MUSIC

Find all of these words in the grid.
Look up, down, across, and diagonally.
Words can run backward as well as forward.

```
D L L O R D N A K C O R
E U E K P R E G G E S A
S O O L T E A R H E A E
Y N A C A H R I S O U L
J F O L K T N A Z F L E
G A R N E E B S L Y E C
A E Z L T E A A N A A T
S P L Z R A M C J C G R
D A R W H E S W I N G O
B C O U N T R Y V H E N
E K R C A L Y P S O R I
A O O A N T B A B E R C
```

| | | |
|---|---|---|
| BALLET | FLAMENCO | REGGAE |
| CALYPSO | FOLK | ROCK AND ROLL |
| COUNTRY | JAZZ | SOUL |
| ELECTRONIC | OPERA | SWING |

# Challenging

## 152: FASTENERS

Find all of these words in the grid.
Look up, down, across, and diagonally.
Words can run backward as well as forward.

```
Z E R O S E J O Y A T N
T L V E P L A E C W E C
S E Y T Y P H J L H C S
F N V E A A T V A G A S
H O B I H T V Z S H L E
C T W U R S T E P K E N
L T S K C B U L C Y O R
A U S M K K E O C E H A
M B C E O M L N E I S H
P J R T Q D N E N A I L
A S E O A O E S T R A P
M E W P L I S T R A M H
```

| BUCKLE | HARNESS | SCREW |
|--------|---------|-------|
| BUTTON | NAIL | SHOELACE |
| CLAMP | PADLOCK | STAPLE |
| CLASP | RIVET | STRAP |

# Challenging

## 153: JUGGLING

Find all of these words in the grid.
Look up, down, across, and diagonally.
Words can run backward as well as forward.

```
I K T H R L U C A T S M
E Q C C L U B S A E D J
R U E I R B E S E A N E
U E K I R L T O Y U A Z
E S M A T T D H J W H O
R N O T U H Y C R P O S
T I I K E N E T K O M E
N K N T E N E A R H W S
S Y R G U H D C S A D O
E A M F S O M U I H P P
S E T A L P R A A P O S
S E R C O N T R O L M W
```

| CATCH | PARTY TRICK | SHOW |
|-------|-------------|------|
| CLUBS | PLATES | SKILL |
| CONTROL | RINGS | SKITTLES |
| HANDS | ROUTINE | THROW |

# Challenging

### 154: HORSES

Find all of these words in the grid.
Look up, down, across, and diagonally.
Words can run backward as well as forward.

```
S P U R R I T S S O F E
E R A A H S T E T E A F
T R A G E A S O E O S L
U T I D B A V H F O A L
S E L L C H S S L A S O
N S E P O L L A G W S E
Z E D O G Y M K H A N A
B C V S B Y E I R E I T
R E T N A C N N N E L R
S T R O T N A L A O E L
I H K H Y K L M C M N Z
G A L L O R A C E D E P
```

| CANTER | GYMKHANA | SHOES |
| --- | --- | --- |
| COLT | HOOVES | STABLE |
| FOAL | MANE | STIRRUPS |
| GALLOP | NEIGH | WHINNY |

# Challenging

## 155: HARRY POTTER

Find all of these words in the grid.
Look up, down, across, and diagonally.
Words can run backward as well as forward.

```
E N O I M R E H H E R E
M U G W G R I C C K E R
W O W E T I C T C L L O
I S O Y A M W I T N G D
Z P A N E R T D C D G E
A U H E D S E D E E U L
R D C A M E T I Y H M B
D M P O G W W U D W K M
H O O M P R G Q O K C U
K R G Z D O I M B O T D
B E Q U I D I D B D B O
H O G W A R T S Y P A B
```

| BROOMSTICK | HEDWIG | MUGGLE |
|------------|--------|--------|
| DOBBY | HERMIONE | QUIDDITCH |
| DUMBLEDORE | HOGWARTS | SPUDMORE |
| HAGRID | MOONDEW | WIZARD |

# Challenging

## 156: VERY BRAVE

Find all of these words in the grid.
Look up, down, across, and diagonally.
Words can run backward as well as forward.

```
C O N F I D E N T B V N
S S P L U C K Y Z H C O
U K S A D V E N T O U E
O E W E L U C K U L G Y
R A P O L E D R S D H I
U B O L D R A T I V E N
T F E A R G A A E A R T
N E Z U E Y R E Z L O R
E S O O J F L S F I I E
V S U D A R I N N A C P
D S G N I R A D I N D I
A U U C S P I R I T E D
```

| ADVENTUROUS | DARING | PLUCKY |
|---|---|---|
| BOLD | FEARLESS | SPIRITED |
| CONFIDENT | HEROIC | UNAFRAID |
| COURAGEOUS | INTREPID | VALIANT |

# Challenging

## 157: FICTIONAL ANIMALS

Find all of these words in the grid.
Look up, down, across, and diagonally.
Words can run backward as well as forward.

```
U M R G M R U D O L P H
R A E B I G O Y B G E D
M H G S M A U E M V R A
P V G M E R A F U J O R
I I I A U F L S D O Y I
G T T R E I R B L R E N
L S G P P E F O A A E O
E K B P E L E I N M N T
S M E A I D G H M C B O
I R A C L P E B L E C I
C S K E N O B M C O T E
U A P U O R O W F O A Y
```

| | | |
|---|---|---|
| ASLAN | EEYORE | ROWF |
| BALOO | FLICKA | RUDOLPH |
| BAMBI | FLIPPER | TIGGER |
| DUMBO | GARFIELD | YOGI BEAR |

# Challenging

## 158: MAKING MOVIES

Find all of these words in the grid.
Look up, down, across, and diagonally.
Words can run backward as well as forward.

```
A C T P R O D U Y R R O
S C O R E N T B B O J I
C E S W B R E A S T C D
E X T R A N Y P A C O U
N J A I L D O K A A S T
E D L T D R T M N E T S
S E R E P T E C H F U G
R O S R P R C A R E M A
O V U M A S T R I Y E H
R N O N U N A R A W S T
E R E E D I R E C T O R
P D S T U D O R I O N F
```

ACTOR           EXTRA           SOUND

CAMERA          PROMPT          STUDIO

COSTUMES        PROPS           TRAILER

DIRECTOR        SCENES          WRITER

# Challenging

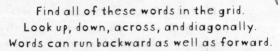

## 159: BITS AND PIECES

Find all of these words in the grid.
Look up, down, across, and diagonally.
Words can run backward as well as forward.

```
S H R E N Y D B A R T A
D U A S L O M I M B L E
P A E Z F I I J K D B Z
D S H G L C U T T I N G
I H E R A V H E A T W K
V R J L K T H E N R E Z
I E K M E E N E O C T F
S D A N L C M E I V L A
I P E P U G E L C A Y R
O A I D A H S A H R A I
N N Y R N H C G S E E U
G N F R O C T I O N P P
```

| | | |
|---|---|---|
| CHUNK | FRAGMENT | PERCENTAGE |
| CUTTING | HALF | RATION |
| DIVISION | HELPING | SHRED |
| FLAKE | LIMB | SLICE |

163

# Challenging

## 160: INVENTIONS

Find all of these words in the grid.
Look up, down, across, and diagonally.
Words can run backward as well as forward.

```
W A L K I E T A L K I E
O V O E C E A C F E Y S
A R E B J L I N E B S J
C T E N I T O S W A S P
A T K L S C E C P O A A
M P O A C E Y M K R E C
E C L B F E O C A E M A
R P I I O C O C L V G P
A L A S E R H W H E E L
A H E P A U C R A W R E
G A H F T D R A D I O L
E R R E T U P M O C Y T
```

| | | |
|---|---|---|
| BICYCLE | COMPUTER | RADIO |
| CAMERA | LASER | ROBOT |
| CLOCK | PARACHUTE | WALKIE TALKIE |
| COMPASS | PLASTIC | WHEEL |

# Challenging

## 161: ISLANDS OF THE PACIFIC

Find all of these words in the grid.
Look up, down, across, and diagonally.
Words can run backward as well as forward.

```
I N U A S S A N M L Q U
G O I S L A R E O N N H
U A O R S E S I E A R A
A U T A U N A V I V K O
M L M U Y S I T E A S A
K I R I O A A J I Q I E
I N I K I B Q D I A L S
D A L X I A O N T F L A
S E I R E K M P A S A F
E N I A A M I S E U W E
R K E H A W A I I P R C
O M P I T C A I R N E U
```

| BIKINI | KIRIBATI | OAHU |
|--------|----------|------|
| FIJI | KODIAK | PITCAIRN |
| GUAM | NASSAU | VANUATU |
| HAWAII | NAURU | WALLIS |

# Challenging

## 162: HAVING NUMBERS

Find all of these words in the grid.
Look up, down, across, and diagonally.
Words can run backward as well as forward.

```
A R L T E L E P H O N E
E A L D P L E P A T H Y
O D A R O S C A L E S C
S N B R A T I O N I E L
T E L K C C I R U L E R
E L O L R V W A T R I P
T A O T E I F A E B D A
E C P L J H O C T I H G
K D R A O B E R O C S E
C A S E L I I C T M H S
I N O A P E R A S E A R
T R E T E M O M R E H T
```

| | | |
|---|---|---|
| CALENDAR | RECEIPT | TELEPHONE |
| CLOCK | RULER | THERMOMETER |
| PAGES | SCALES | TICKET |
| POOL BALL | SCOREBOARD | WATCH |

# Challenging

**163: BOATS**

Find all of these words in the grid.
Look up, down, across, and diagonally.
Words can run backward as well as forward.

```
T R E E A R K E S T O R
E F T G D V R T K U H C
Y B L H R M E F R E R A
T T A E C A L W A R E A
T A G T M A B B S W E R
C O N E T A Y F H A T F
J B R K B L R E A V H E
A G E J E I E M O E U R
M N R B G R P S N G A R
B O K A Y A K A H F R Y
E L T K U E O H T I N Y
O E D S L I N E R C P A
```

| | | |
|---|---|---|
| BARGE | KAYAK | RAFT |
| BATTLESHIP | LINER | STEAMER |
| FERRY | LONGBOAT | TANKER |
| FRIGATE | NOAH'S ARK | YACHT |

# Challenging

## 164: SEWING

Find all of these words in the grid.
Look up, down, across, and diagonally.
Words can run backward as well as forward.

```
B N O T T O C B Q U I E
S O T T O N E S U Y R L
C O Y T A P E Y I R L D
I E R S A H B R L T V E
E A R T C A G E T S U E
S L C T L E E D I E D N
E H I O F R E I N P A Y
C T H R E A D O G A R L
S Y D I N U E R P T N N
H E M M I N G B B I I O
R E D V E R E M M I N E
G N I K C A T E Z Z G S
```

| COTTON | NEEDLE | STITCHES |
| DARNING | PATCH | TACKING |
| EMBROIDERY | PINS | TAPESTRY |
| HEMMING | QUILTING | THREAD |

# Challenging

## 165: HEADGEAR

Find all of these words in the grid.
Look up, down, across, and diagonally.
Words can run backward as well as forward.

```
N L S O M B R E R O E T
O E A S E B E R E L B N
S F T E A B A T E L A R
T E E A O R E B A R S F
E E N H Z A N C T E E
T R N B R N C I E I B D
S E B O N N I R T K A O
T I R E S M E A L H L R
F L I M D B S F R O L A
A K L U M R A Y Z O C E
H E L M E T E V A D A L
K N A B R U T F E O P E
```

| BASEBALL CAP | HELMET | STETSON |
| BERET | HOOD | TIARA |
| BONNET | RAIN HAT | TURBAN |
| FEDORA | SOMBRERO | YARMULKA |

# Challenging

## 166: DOG BREEDS

Find all of these words in the grid.
Look up, down, across, and diagonally.
Words can run backward as well as forward.

```
R C A N S A L U K I E O
N O R W E R C M F R L U
N B D E D E E F B E D P
A T E A A M I I F T O O
M U E S R T O R R D O F
R T H P S B N A I R P D
E E N A D T A E R G E Z
B P M N U J L L S Y C T
O P J I O H R B O A O R
D I O E M T I M B A R E
T H D L R B A H G M G F
Y W H I P S E T C V I E
```

| | | |
|---|---|---|
| CHIHUAHUA | LABRADOR | SAMOYED |
| CORGI | MASTIFF | SPANIEL |
| DOBERMANN | POODLE | TERRIER |
| GREAT DANE | SALUKI | WHIPPET |

# Challenging

## 167: PEOPLE IN UNIFORM

Find all of these words in the grid.
Look up, down, across, and diagonally.
Words can run backward as well as forward.

```
E F E I G H T E R L Q R
E S A S T A G V A I E R
A W R P G U A R D V H E
L E W U I Y I O I S A T
S L O D N M J R D F O H
P O E E D G D T S L K G
L Y L A X S E A I W A I
A T P D U N E P O A S F
M E P B I A D O R I N E
O J O C K E Y E R T A R
R O L I A S R E R E Y I
F O O T B A L L E R W F
```

| | | |
|---|---|---|
| ADMIRAL | GUARD | PILOT |
| BUS DRIVER | GUIDE | SAILOR |
| FIREFIGHTER | JOCKEY | SOLDIER |
| FOOTBALLER | NURSE | WAITER |

# Challenging

## 168: NURSERY RHYMES AND STORIES

Find all of these words in the grid.
Look up, down, across, and diagonally.
Words can run backward as well as forward.

```
G R E T E L G D S N L G
L S O E U E B A F E A R
A O B C N L N B Z E L A
M I D I E L B N P A L N
F A E N B H U I U A N H
N A D D J P E S D A M A
E I I E A I R D T C P N
H F B R S E I N S E R S
D E M E Y N A J O L L E
E G O L D I L O C K S L
R E X L G R E T L E S R
L C J A C K S P R A T K
```

| | | |
|---|---|---|
| ALADDIN | GIANT | JACK SPRAT |
| CINDERELLA | GOLDILOCKS | RAPUNZEL |
| FAIRY | GRETEL | RED HEN |
| GENIE | HANSEL | SINBAD |

# Challenging

## 169: SANTA AND HIS REINDEER

Find all of these words in the grid.
Look up, down, across, and diagonally.
Words can run backward as well as forward.

```
B N E X I V R C O M T E
B V S A K C E R U P D K
P L G A E R H U R P F X
R N I A C G U A E H I U
E U A T I K N C E R A D
S T D E Z C D A S H E R
E W L O E E V E O D O D
N S O R L Y N E V H A J
T N I V U P E F B N R B
S P R E S E H S C U W V
D O N N E R T E M O C J
O P R E S A R U D O R W
```

BLITZEN          DASHER           RUDOLPH

COMET            DONNER           SACK

CUPID            PRANCER          SLEIGH

DANCER           PRESENTS         VIXEN

# Solutions

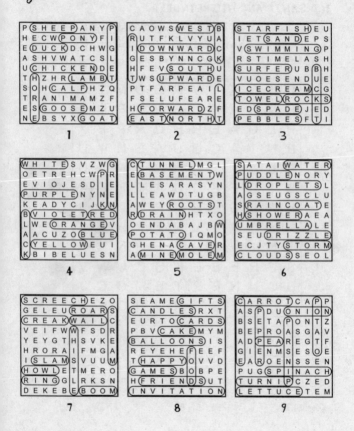

**1**
```
P S H E E P A N Y P
H E C W P O N Y F I
E D U C K D C H W G
A S H V W A T C S L
U C H I C K E N D E
T H Z H R L A M B T
S O H C A L F H Z Q
T R A N I M A M Z F
E S G O O S E M Z U
N E B S Y X G O A T
```

**2**
```
C A O W S W E S T B
R U T F K L V Y U A
I D O W N W A R D C
G E S B Y N N C G K
H F E V S O U T H U
T W S U P W A R D E
P T F A R P E A I L
F S E L U F E A R E
H F O R W A R D Z F
E A S T N O R T H T
```

**3**
```
S T A R F I S H E U
I E T S A N D E P S
V S W I M M I N G P
R S T I M E L A S H
S U R F E R U B B H
V U O E S E N D U E
I C E C R E A M C G
T O W E L R O C K S
E D S P A D E J E D
P E B B L E S F T I
```

**4**
```
W H I T E S V Z W G
O E T R E H C W P R
E V I O J E S D I E
P U R P L E N Y N E
K E A D Y C I J K N
B V I O L E T R E D
L W E O R A N G E V
A A C U Z O B L U E
C Y E L L O W E U I
K B I B E L U E S N
```

**5**
```
C T U N N E L M G L
E B A S E M E N T W
L L E S A R A S Y N
L L E A W D T U G B
A W E Y R O O T S T
R D R A I N H T X O
O E N D A B A J B W
P O T A T O I Q M O
G H E N A C A V E R
A M I N E M O L E M
```

**6**
```
S A T A I W A T E R
P U D D L E N O R Y
L D R O P L E T S L
A G S E U G S C L U
S R A I N C O A T E
H S H O W E R A E A
U M B R E L L A L E
S E U D R I Z Z L E
E C J T Y S T O R M
C L O U D S S E O L
```

**7**
```
S C R E E C H E Z O
G E L E U R O A R S
C R E A K W A I L C
V E I F W W F S D R
Y E Y G T H S V K E
H R O R A I F M G A
I S L A M S V U U M
H O W L E T M E R O
R I N G G L R K S N
D E K E B E B O O M
```

**8**
```
S E A M E G I F T S
C A N D L E S R X T
E U R T O C A R D S
P B V C A K E M Y M
B A L L O O N S I S
R E Y E H E F E E F
T H A P P Y O V V D
G A M E S B O B P E
H F R I E N D S U T
I N V I T A T I O N
```

**9**
```
C A R R O T C A P P
A S P D U O N I O N
B S E T A P O N T Z
B E P R O A S G A V
A D P E A R E G T F
G I E N M S E S O E
E A R O E N S S E N
P U G S P I N A C H
T U R N I P C Z E D
L E T T U C E T E M
```

# Solutions

```
N V F B I C Y C L E
R E P E D A L S G E
H E L M E T A Y O S
P O E P A S E P R P
V O Z Y B E L L I E
S A D D L E I U E M
L I G H T S P J V P
L E W R B R A K E S
Y U D W H E E L S H
G E A R S C H A I N
```
10

```
H I G H W I R E T B
C L O W N S M R I I
T R I C K S C C G G
P A R A D E C A H T
P R H E P L T E T O
B A L L O O N S R P
T G E P K O I S O E
E N I M A G I C P H
R I N G M A S T E R
T R A P E Z E R D E
```
11

```
F I Z Z I N G S Z G
S P A R K L E R V V
T U E L E V E V B F
F T B W H O O S H L
I E V X F L A R E I
D I S P L A Y O Y G
K A E A E U F C J H
F I R E W O R K S T
B A N G E R E E S S
N O I S Y Y U T E D
```
12

```
F A W N P I G L E T
N E T I R A S E P V
D U C K L I N G U L
K I T T E N E V P F
K U B E Y U B R P C
H C O W G U S A Y H
F T A D P O L E W I
O G O E U I Z T C C
A E C U B L K R A K
L J E M R L A M B P
```
13

```
E C A N D Y M A S E
S H Z G I F T S A R
A H O L L Y W E S O
N F L L Q C A R D S
T R E E O L S E J T
A W U L I G H T S P
V W G T E A S P A N
U S O C B T T O Y S
L G L F P R A P J H
E C D E F M R V A E
```
14

```
P L A N E T S L X I
H T L B S M O O N B
J U P I T E R M M Q
P L U T O N Z Y O J
P A H L X C M A R S
U N E P T U N E R S
E U Y I Y T R A E T
I Y E M S U N I A A
S A T U R N D Z R R
U N E L V E N U S S
```
15

```
O S T R I C H E J H
S T R B E C C A F M
C G O O S E I G A O
W C O T A M V L I T
I O T M Y S M E R H
M E R A C R O W Y L
D R A G O N F L Y J
N P K A R A H O D O
B U T T E R F L Y F
A N G E L U B I R D
```
16

```
H E F F A L U M P G
U J W I N N E L I E
N P E P V E X R O O
N F T I G G E R I R
Y G L G R A B B I T
R O E L E E Y O R E
Y U E E E C A W A S
F X A T I N K L H U
K A N G A S K A N N
W I N N I E S P H C
```
17

```
M B U T T E R F L Y
I C E N T I P E D E
L M I J G A E S N J
L A N T R C W S F S
I W O R M E I L O P
P E O R M F Q U E I
E F E A R W I G N D
D I B E E T L E T E
E F E R H E F G W R
H A U I V S N A I L
```
18

# Solutions

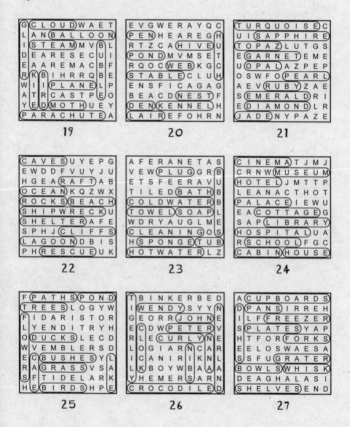

**19**

```
G C L O U D W A E T
L A N B A L L O O N
I S T E A M M V B L
D E A R E S E C U I
E A A R E M A C B F
R K B I H R R Q B E
W I I P L A N E L P
A T R C A S T P E O
Y E D M O T H U E Y
P A R A C H U T E A
```

**20**

```
E V G W E R A Y Q C
P E N H E A R E G H
R T Z C A H I V E U
P O N D M V M S E T
R Q O C W E B K G C
S T A B L E C L U H
E N S F I C A G A G
B E A C D N E S T F
D E N K E N N E L H
L A I R E F O H R N
```

**21**

```
T U R Q U O I S E C
U I S A P P H I R E
T O P A Z L U T G S
E G A R N E T E M E
U O P A L A Z P E P
O S W F O P E A R L
A E V R U B Y Z A E
S E M E R A L D R I
E D I A M O N D L R
J A D E N Y P A Z E
```

**22**

```
C A V E S U Y E P G
E W D D F V U Y J U
H G E A R A F T A B
O C E A N K Q Z W X
R O C K S B E A C H
S H I P W R E C K U
S H E L T E R A F E
S P H J C L I F F S
L A G O O N D B I S
P H R E S C U E U K
```

**23**

```
A F E R A N E T A S
V E W P L U G G R B
E T S F E E R A V U
T I L E D B A T H B
C O L D W A T E R L
T O W E L S O A P L
W D R Y A U G L M E
C L E A N I N G O S
H S P O N G E T U B
H O T W A T E R L Z
```

**24**

```
C I N E M A T J M J
C R N W M U S E U M
H O T E L J M T T P
L E A N A C T H O T
P A L A C E I E W U
E A C O T T A G E G
S A P L I B R A R Y
H O S P I T A L U A
R S C H O O L F G C
C A B I N H O U S E
```

**25**

```
F P A T H S P O N D
T R E E S L O G Y W
F I D A R I S T O R
L Y E N D I T R Y H
O D U C K S L E C D
W V E M B L E R S D
E C B U S H E S Y L
R A G R A S S V S A
S F T I D E L A R K
H E B I R D S H P E
```

**26**

```
T B I N K E R B E D
I W E N D Y S Y Y N
G E O R R J O H N E
E C D W P E T E R V
R L E C U R L Y N E
L O G I A R N C A R
I C A N I R I K N L
L K B O Y W B A A A
Y H E M E R S A R N
C R O C O D I L E D
```

**27**

```
A C U P B O A R D S
D P A N S I R R E H
I L F F R E E Z E R
S P L A T E S Y A P
H T F O R F O R K S
E E L O S W A E S A
S S F U G R A T E R
B O W L S W H I S K
D E A G H A L A S I
S H E L V E S E N D
```

# Solutions

```
V A S T G R E A T H
M F S J I I P V S U
A A O Y A F E A Y G
M N A B N R N P V E
M U E C T R I L J J
O E S T G J U M B O
T I M M E N S E L S
H M A S S I V E M K
H I C W B I G E L A
G E N O R M O U S W
```
28

```
E N E G N I L T X Y
S T R I O B Z R P C
A I R P O R T A A A
O B U R E C S I Q M
T E N C P L A N E E
A S W I M S U I T R
X T O R T O I S H A
I H O T E L M A P S
S U I T C A S E K U
U N I S C E N E R Y
```
29

```
D U C K L I N G C O
C H I C K S C E N A
D A N D E L I O N E
L E N E G G Y O L K
D B U T T E R C U P
C A N A R Y X I L A
O N C C H E E S E I
D A F F O D I L M B
I N T R A S E W O E
V A B E N E N S N E
```
30

```
C T C A L A R Y C X
H S N O W M A N H V
R E I N A R I Y I I
I I C I C L E D L D
S K A T I N G N L L
T T I F R O S T Y S
M F R E E Z I N G C
A G R I N D L E X A
S U S S K I I N G R
S N O W B A L L T F
```
31

```
F R I E N D L Y S T
C L O C T E D D Y H
I J E R A N E A R N
E C U D D L Y F U R
A I A H P A W S E G
R X U L D S U F H E
S R I B B O N F B C
T W E B R E N B Y U
R O V F L U F F Y T
S Q U E A K E R T E
```
32

```
G R U M P Y S A N P
B L O O A H A P P Y
S L E E P Y O A S E
E F A I R E S T T E
L E I B A S H F U L
D O C O E T R E R D
E N U M I R R O R A
D O P E Y A V E R A
M I S T Y A P P L E
W E B N S N E E Z Y
```
33

```
C R A B B I T R E C
R S E M K I T T E N
O H O R S E W E R S
G C M H A M S T E R
U A H E M D O G E R
K T G N O D A D V E
P U P P Y U E N A R
V I S T U C F R O G
T I E L O K L P X S
I A G O L D F I S H
```
34

```
U F T O S A T I N E
O L V E L V E T E M
N Y L O N G Q V L E
T R I S C O T T O N
G E S K S I L K N D
A M V B C Z B C D O
I L L I N E N F E Y
S A B A I S X E N N
E C C V W O O L I A
D E B E E J L T M M
```
35

```
D A T R I A N G L E
R I H A R P D R U M
E H E E S I O B O E
C O R D E C D G F B
O R N O R G A N L A
R N B A N J O G U H
D R N P S E R A T E
E D C L A R I N E T
R A Q N L U U T V H
E R Y E E T R I A N
```
36

# Solutions

**37**

```
B L E M O N A D E O
U E S A L A D C M T
T N S G F R U I T U
T E E S E C L O T H
E T M A L E S E C A
R P L E A B R E A D
W O N E Y E U S K W
F A R F P L A T E S
S C H E E S E Y S C
S A N D W I C H E S
```

**38**

```
G E N T L E D O R A
V E L V E T Y E A L
S H O I D S I L K Y
F S Q U I S H Y E L
L E B G F L E E C Y
U G S U L L D I F D
F G E R I S A N U O
F E A T H E R Y R W
Y E D M P E T O R N
S M O O T H R O Y Y
```

**39**

```
R A I N D R O P T G
O E B K C H I C K N
U N S T A V F L E A
C P L E F A I R Y Y
R T M W B I M Y A W
U M A N T D O T M R
M E Y B E D A R I E
B L V A D M E K E E
I F M K H S E E D A
S N O W F L A K E R
```

**40**

```
C A R A O N I O N T
E K S T E R I N P O
L O X T A I L G E M
E P O T A T O E N A
R M U S H R O O M T
Y H U I I D A N E O
V E G E T A B L E A
P U M P K I N P O P
P E R S A T U P E A
L E Y C H I C K E N
```

**41**

```
W I Z A R D S J W S
I Z A T Z S P N W E
T F A I R E E R A E
C A E L V C L E N V
H R L R F R L A D I
A P I X I E S V E C
E L V E S T E O A Z
E S M A G I C I A N
N O N F A I R I E S
T R I C K S N E C E
```

**42**

```
O G O L D S H I P S
P I R A E G T C A S
E Y E P A T C H R I
O F E R N A T T R L
E J E W E L S E O V
R R F B O W S E T E
C A P T A I N U D R
T J C H E S D R N Y
E M G N E A R M A P
O C E A N C H E S T
```

**43**

```
I Y E K W A T E R S
N I O T A F D Y O P
N B U C K E T H R O
H R A T E I N G Y N
P O L I S H E N E G
Z C L E A N I N G E
S K F W H E E L S S
O E A W I N D O W S
A S H I N E J B Y C
P S R I N S I N G E
```

**44**

```
K E Y S K E P C B N
T R E A S U R E U M
S A S L E E P U T E
H O M E W O R K T M
E T T A S E S A O O
H E E L M G B I N R
S M E A A A B E E Y
E P T B H M O N E Y
O E H A P E U S E G
P R O V E R A N C E
```

**45**

```
E X E M Y S H I P R
C Y A C H T T B K O
A H Y E W N R I I H C
N F N S B W A C E V E
O C U D V K I Y V E T
E C T A X I N C C T
U R W B O A T L H P
J H O R S E L E L E
E I E L I Y A E H T
Q E Z T L P L A N E
```

# Solutions

```
B O H I S T O R Y Y
O Y E C A S T N S Y
O E L A D E S K Y T
K L A A B C A R E B
S G E O G R A P H Y
C L A S S D E A K S
L E A R N I N G E P
T E A C H E R E I O
M U S I C U E R V R
G R E A D I N G Q T
        46
```

```
E R T D A T E S N W
T U E S A J S E E E
S A T U R D A Y H E
T U E S D A Y T U K
W E D N E S D A Y S
I E L F R I D A Y E
T H U R S D A Y W K
M O N D M O N T H S
M O N D A Y E E N A
S U N D A Y K A E S
        47
```

```
A P P L E S L O E T
C O R N M A R A O S
P T L T A Y A T D E
J V T G I E R S U A
G H U Y Z E K X F T
R R E M E T N U T S
A L E A V E S G E S
S B M E A S D A S A
S D W H E A T E A N
S E E D S U E H A Y
        48
```

```
P I N E A P P L E E
T F C P D R E A S Y
O H M E H I A H A M
M E C P T F J O E H
A E H P U E A T U D
T S E E N C R U S T
O A E R A A R E R E
E I S S O N I O N S
S C E O L I V E S B
M U S H R O O M S S
        49
```

```
C A R I A G K V G C
R S P R I N C E P A
M I D N I G H T A R
D R E S S E U L L R
G N A S E T A F A I
Q U E E N P I R C A
B A L L P A L C E G
R A G S M I C E S E
S L I P P E R K N K
S Y R L I P E T E R
        50
```

```
A L L I G A T O R H
T T E R R A P I N E
O T E R R L Y L C W
R C A V I P E R G W
T U R T L E D P E D
O U E D J B S O C E
I G U A N A N Q K T
S R A J P Y T H O N
E C R O C O D I L E
L I Z A R D C L A R
        51
```

```
C L A V E N D E R E
R S R I L I P U R A
O R C H I D L A P O
C D A F F O D I L P
U Y A M C O V E R P
S N O W D R O P N V
H D A I S Y I R I S
S U N F L O W E R L
L D E R A L I L Y O
N R P O P P Y A P Y
        52
```

```
E B A S E B A L L T
G E R E S H O S A E
D E B B T E N N I S
F M B O W L I N G T
S K I T T L E S O R
H O C K E Y C L L E
F O O T B A L L F G
B A S K E T B A L L
V P O L O O E R A L
R I N P O O L N C E
        53
```

```
F I A P P L D E N H
M O R C H A R D C W
C O R E N S E E D U
T R E E R G R E E N
P E E L J U I C Y S
S T R E R L S C I T
A I Y M E E A S E E
P B L O S S O M S M
E I I B K F R C K E
D Z O B R E D P Y S
        54
```

# Solutions

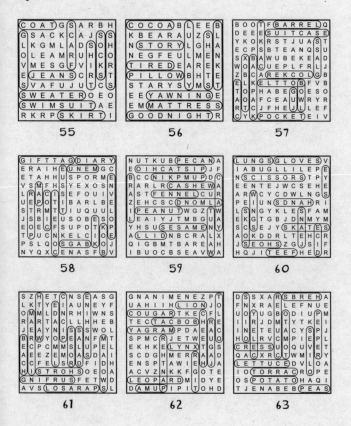

**55**

```
C O A T G S A R B H
G S A C K C A J S S
L K G M L A D S O H
O L E A M R U H C O
V M E S G F V I K R
E J E A N S C R S T
S V A F U J U T C S
S W E A T E R O E O
S W I M S U I T A E
R K R P S K I R T I
```

**56**

```
C O C O A B L E E B
K B E A R A U Z S L
N S T O R Y L G H A
N E G F E U L M E N
T I R E D E A R E K
P I L L O W B H T E
S T A R Y S M Y M S
E E Y A W N I N G E
E M M A T T R E S S
G O O D N I G H T R
```

**57**

```
B O O T F B A R R E L Q
D E E E S U I T C A S E
Y K O K R S T J U A S T
E C P S B T E A N Q S U
S X B A W U B E K E A D
W O A C U E P L F R L J
Z B C A R E K C O L G B
E L K E L T T O B F V B
T O P H A B E G O E O A
O A F C E A U W R Y R
A R T C J F H E U L L E F
C Y K P O C K E T E I V
```

**58**

```
G I F T T A G D I A R Y
E R A I H E U N E M G C
E T A H H U S P O R M E
V S M F H S Y E X O S N
L R A C I S E F O U I V
U E P O T I B A R L B E
S T R M T T I U Q U U L
J S B I E U S O B E S O
E O E C F S U P D T K P
T P U C N K E L C I O E
P S L Q O S G A B K O J
N Y Q X C E N A S F B V
```

**59**

```
N U T K U B P E C A N A
E O I H C A T S I P J F
B C C N I K P M U P D C
R A R L R C A S H E W A
A S T F E N N E L C U R
Z E H C S C D N O M L A
I P E A N U T W G Z T W
L E A I Y J T M B G U A
Y H S U S E S A M E N Y
A L L I D N B C R A L X
Q I G B M T B A R E A H
I B U O C B S E A V W A
```

**60**

```
L U N G S G L O V E S V
I A B U G L L I L E P E
N S C I S S O R S T P Y
E E N T E J W C S E H E
A R W C Y C D W L N G S
P E I U N S D N A H R I
L S N G Y K L E S F A M
E K G T G B J D N M Y M
S C S E J Y S K A T E S
A O K D D R L T E H C R
J S E O H S Z G U S I F
H Q J I T E E F H E D R
```

**61**

```
S Z H E T C N S E A S G
L K T Y E I A U N E Y F
O M M L D N R H I W N S
R A R T A C L L H E E B
J E A Y N I S S W O L
B R W Y O P E A N F M T
E C P C M M S L U P E L
A E E Z E M O A S D A I
C C F E L S R D F I D H
H U S T R O H S O E O A
G N I F R U S F E T W D
A V S L O S A R A P S L
```

**62**

```
G N A N I M E N E Z P T
U A H I I H L I O N J O
C O U G A R T K E C F L
T E C T A C B O B H R E
Y A G R A M P D A E A C
S P M C R J E T W E U O
E K H K E L Y N X T G S
S C D G H M E R R A A D
E N S P T A W I E H J A
A C V Z N K K F G O T E
L E O P A R D M I D Y E
D A M U P I P I T O H D
```

**63**

```
D S S X A R S B R E H A
F N X R A E L E F N U E
U O Y U G B O D I U P M
I I R J D M T Y T K E I
I N E T E U A C Y S P J
H O L R V C M P U E I P L
C R E S S U O Q U V E T
Q A C X C T W M I R Y
L E T T U C E D V L O A
I O T O R R A C R O P E
O S P O T A T O H A Q I
T J E N A B E B P E A S
```

# Solutions

64

65

66

67

68

69

70

71

72

# Solutions

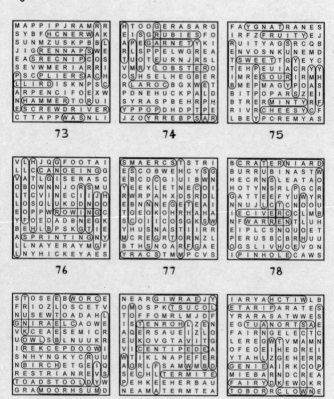

73

74

75

76

77

78

79

80

81

# Solutions

**82**

```
M D S M I T H E R S U K
I F L D N O M A R G E R
L S E D E Y R S K O S U
H E N G L T E I I J M S
E Y N U S S J L S E W Y
D M Y E O U C O S G H R
A O T S N R U B R M T F
T U R J H K I M U N Y A
A R A J I M E I B R R E
R G B W A U P J C K W I
E O D E S U O H L I M E
N I T R A M G E L E I S
```

**83**

```
L L R O T O R O W A R A
O L L I M D N I W H E T
O I J M E W T S S T F H
P R O P E L L E R R S Y
L D E F E S A C A A A G
R O G J T F I P C E T E
I J O Y E R U W I E E E
H E K N M E C H N H L E
W B A M O V I I I G T L E
E Y R O C D E S C F I F
H L T O N U R K A N T N
B E U N E R A Y R W E D
```

**84**

```
T S I L E V O N E R S A
B H A S Y E H O E N X K
G E D I T O R C L E R K
C R A T H O R A A F N T
T E A C H E R R G E L N
E P R O F E S S O R K E
O O U R E S O P M O C M
P R A O T S I R A I D U
Y T F H E L E E A N D T
E E A T O R E S A B B S
S R J U N E V E L I S T
E H N A I R O T S I H J
```

**85**

```
A R N A Y M M U M A G E
R O U A R S P H I N X S
T A M T E A P L E D S U
A M A N F L J D G I W R
P Y H P Y R A M I D S Y
O N K V F B N P D N A P
E I N B M O T H G A Z A
L L A G B A R A C S J P
C E T Q M P Y R M A R I
D F U U E V I A Z I G O
Y P T H V A F O V A Z Z
S E L P M E T H W U R E
```

**86**

```
K C H O C A C O H I S Y
G O H C R E G B A E C O
V C Y E N G G G E O Y O H
U O V K E S E S W E E T
M A L A M M R M A S P F
C R U C A O E O E J Q A
H E H C E O T O C I W W
I C N A R A S T U C H R
C L E N C E A H A E I D
E A U D E J E R S S T A
A I L Y C V K E B F E R
M R G N I K N I R D F K
```

**87**

```
S K D U H G P W D F W S
P I R V H N E A N L O H
L M A B L I M K E U R A
A S U A A D E A P M M L
S G G T H A D V E E Q L
H P E H O W J R E T A W
M T F A Y I B H D B V I
W H I S T L E Q D K T E
A I L F L W A R C L P N
N S H A L L O W E N D H
B D I V I N G B O A R D
G N I H T A B E C O L D
```

**88**

```
F A R M W K E A D O C O
O U T I O D S I K F P S
T E E R D R O T A N W J
R D I B A A S D L E I F
O I F R E Y E S I D P O
U T T E M M A R L E J R
G C R M E R U T S A P C
H H A K P A B A R N S H
S E C N E F R I H K P A
C S T J O R C H A O O R
K O O F E R A N S Z R D
W O R C E R A C S T C M
```

**89**

```
L H P Y J A M H O N E Y
O S T L B P E A X W A X
Y R N L N P O L L E N W
A E E E E U H G M H U T
R W V J E E E U Q W E M
Y O G L U R Y Y K O N O
E L N A Q L N H E R O N
L F I Y U E O I V K R I
E K Z O E M L V A E D S
M I Z R N O O E B R U E
A B U R A T C E N A C P
U I B V R E R N C B A N
```

**90**

```
N E G A H N E P O C B V
F U N S T O C K H O L M
D I R D A M S T O C K S
L Z S I R A P D E S A J
O K I V A J K Y E R A H
N E L O N D N V X H T P
D O C O R E N H A G H M
O S R M O S C O W V E E
N L A N O T T A W A N S
Z O R E Y J K A V W S T
C D N O T G N I H S A W
W I N I K N I S L E H C
```

# Solutions

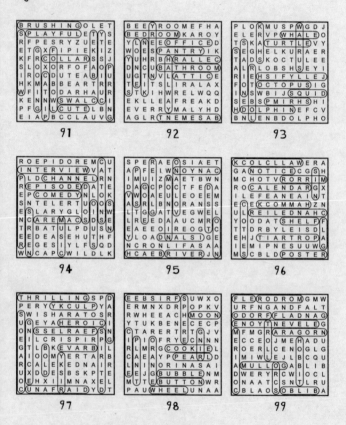

91

92

93

94

95

96

97

98

99

**100**

```
C A B I N B O Y Y T L X
H C D N N U G N E B O F
E K N E G A O H N E U L
T I A R E V D E W N N I
S R L U V E H S A G X N
Y C S S M T U D L O V T
O O U A E L I V E S E Y
H M R E R E G A R E I R
O P K R B E D Z T M I I
H A Z T O R R A P N Y L
O S J I M H A W K I N S
E S H I S P A N I O L A
```

**101**

```
T W I L L O W O L L O A
U H J B E E C H L S A S
N I F C A V E C A U S Y
T C E D A R K I R O E C
S K H N I F E D C S E A
E O A P H U H P H S L M
H R Z R E S T O P H P O
C Y E B O I S A K C A R
O M L A P E T A D R M E
N I F E R A T I N I Y T
T I I N B E L L C B M T
G L E U C A L Y P T U S
```

**102**

```
V U E M A N I R U S B Z
E T O G C O L O M B I A
N T U U R U G U A Y M C
E P A F G U Y A N A J H
R O D A U C E R N E B I
F V O L I V S G P S O L
A L E U Z E N E V A L E
R T B P E R U N U C I I
U N U J N T E N M H S O
Y P E R A N F I P I I A
C B R A Z I L N I L A M
R Y A U G A R A P T A K
```

**103**

```
K R A B E E R T S L I M
O R E N E T O M A T O P
E G N A R O N I O N N M
V M O O R H S U M R I I
G Z E L P P A E G E S R
A E C L M G Y T G P P H
R M L E B A L N E G D S
O E M H O N H I D K E S
N D T S P O T A T O F E
D S E G C T D P G U I V
I O E G C A R R O T O I
S F Z E J H M H A P I Y E
```

**104**

```
S J U G G L E R S E R U
E L I M E S R E C N A D
T E G D I S P L A Y V S
T S V S T R E E M T S A
E E R C O S T U M E S R
R S T A B O R C A D N G
O R S L Y O D I J A H I
J O N F D J R J E R U D
A H W L E V U F E A V R
M T O A A S M P E P S A
M F L G E E S H E P B M
Y A C S P A R I N A T E
```

**105**

```
V O S T R E E M O A S I
E D F A L L I D E O B S
T R A I N F A L L W D N
N E C T R I D E K H Y I
E S J B R O O K C I R A
R Y C E X W D F I R A T
R E O H A A L U R L U N
U G A S T V A Y T P T U
C Y S N U E N M H O S O
J E I U F S A E E O E F
B A S G T O C H R U M E
L U W A T E R F A L L N
```

**106**

```
M H S I N G I N G B P H
B E D R O O M Y T B A U
G A M E R I T A T I O D
S C A G F R I E N D S O
E H G N I Y A L P T R A
I A C I C Q F E D A L I
R T I L Y S W O L L I P
O T S G N J E W W K U C
T I U G S E M A G I L A
S N M C E S T E N M M K
K G V G O I P E R G N E
W F G E M E S L E P L S
```

**107**

```
G A M E O P O T T W E R
N I N H E J I G S A W S
I S I N G I N G F L P G
W T E P F S P B G K E N
O P O T T E R Y N I G I
R G N L G L M A I N N I
V N A E N Z A P D G I K
Y I C S I Z E W I R T S
I D E A K U L L A I N B
L I E Z I P E G R T I J
T R A B H D V B B E A N
G N I W E S Q P U S P Z
```

**108**

```
S S E H C U D O F W E D
W A L S U R O A L A E E
V E N D I N A H C L A N
E R R S E M K N I R D Y
Y T R A P A E T K U D E
E R A H H C R A M S S A
V E L C A L I C E A T E
E G C A R P E N T E R M
I A C F C R O Q U E T N
D R E T T A H D A M D L
T E A P A R T E A T M E
V C A T E R P I L L A R
```

# Solutions

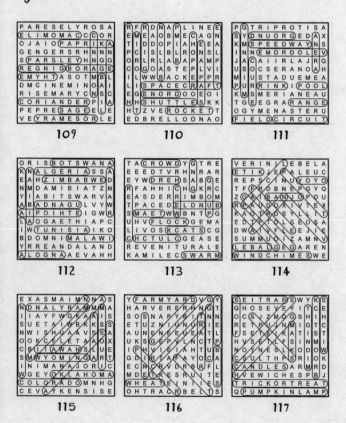

**109**

**110**

**111**

**112**

**113**

**114**

**115**

**116**

**117**

# Solutions

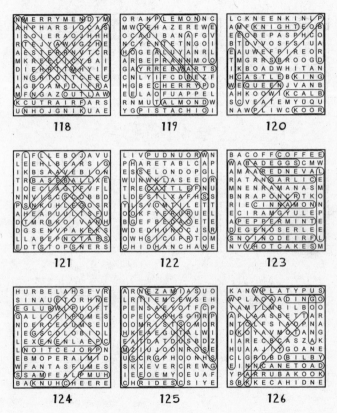

118

119

120

121

122

123

124

125

126

# Solutions

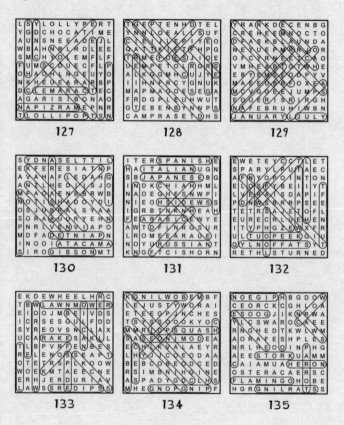

127

128

129

130

131

132

133

134

135

# Solutions

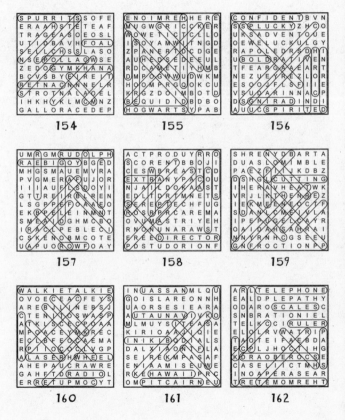

154

155

156

157

158

159

160

161

162

# Solutions

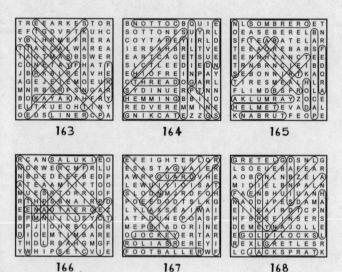

163

164

165

166

167

168

169

# Solutions

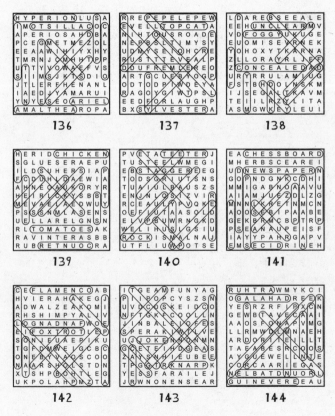

136

137

138

139

140

141

142

143

144

189

# Solutions

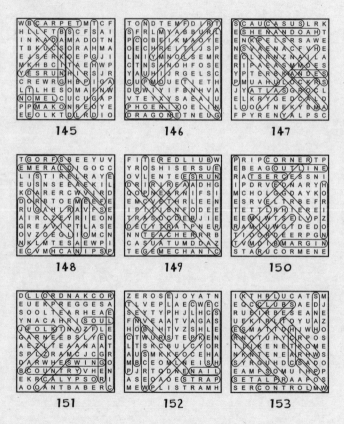

145

146

147

148

149

150

151

152

153